Mills & Boon Classics

A chance to read and collect some of the best-loved novels from Mills & Boon—the world's largest publisher of romantic fiction.

Every month, four titles by favourite Mills & Boon authors will be re-published in the *Classics* series.

A list of other titles in the *Classics* series can be found at the end of this book.

Kay Thorpe

THE IRON MAN

MILLS & BOON LIMITED
LONDON · TORONTO

First published 1974
Australian copyright 1980
Philippine copyright 1980
This edition 1980

© Kay Thorpe 1974

ISBN 0 263 73476 5

Set in Linotype Baskerville 11 on 12 pt.

Made and printed in Great Britain by Richard Clay (The Chaucer Press) Ltd, Bungay, Suffolk

CHAPTER ONE

FOR most of the hundred or so miles up from Freetown the land had been green and forested. Ahead, where the mine workings began, lay desolation and dust, a lunar landscape peopled by giant machines which bit into the tiered grey cliffs like growling predators. Flakes of metal hung in glistening clouds in the air, shrouding the moving, dotted figures of the men at work on the site, rising above the complex of tin buildings climbing up the lower slopes of the hill, settling over the moving belts, railway waggons and grey heaps of core at its base.

Alighting from the battered Land-Rover at the main gate of the site, Kim eased the waistband of her slacks away from her skin and thought longingly of cool showers and fragrant soap. The last few hours had been a nightmare of sticky heat; already she could feel the beginnings of a rash about her waist, and knew that the sooner she got something on it in this climate the better. That, however, would have to wait for a while. There were other more important things she had to see to first.

The guard on duty in the gatehouse was African. He had stared without moving when she got out of the car, and now he continued to regard her with curious eyes as she walked up to the open window.

'I'm looking for Christopher Adams,' Kim said

clearly. 'Can you tell me where I can find him, please?'

The man slowly shook his head, then reached out and lifted the telephone receiver close to hand. He spoke into it briefly, voice muffled by the glass partition, listened a moment, then replaced it on its rest.

'The boss is coming,' he announced. 'He say for you to wait here.'

There wasn't really very much else she could do, Kim supposed. And at least the man in charge would be able to tell her what she wanted to know without further delay. Something had to have happened to Chris, of course. The question was what? She tried to keep the all too familiar fear at bay in her mind. Of course he was still alive. If there had been any kind of accident the authorities here would have informed her of it. No, whatever the explanation for his lack of communication these last two months it had to be something else. Chris would never have acted this way without good reason—very good reason. It wasn't in him to simply cut contact because he had changed his mind about wanting to marry her. He would have written and told her straight out.

A car was coming fast down the road from the nearest group of tin buildings. It drew to a skidding halt on the far side of the barrier and a man got out from behind the wheel. He was big and powerful-looking, the rolled sleeves of his denim shirt revealing muscular forearms. He pushed the dusty slouch hat he wore to the back of his head as he studied her narrowly across the ten feet of space between them.

'I'm Dave Nelson,' he said. 'Who are you?'

'Kimberley Freeman.' Her chin tilted a little at his tone. 'I'm Chris Adams's fiancée. Can I see him?'

There was a brief pause, and the strongly carved mouth seemed to harden still further. 'He isn't here,' he said. 'He hasn't been here for the last five weeks. If I were you I'd get back to where you came from.'

Kim stared at him. 'Not here? Then where is he? You must know!'

One dark eyebrow lifted sardonically. 'Why must I?'

'Because he worked here,' she burst out. 'Something has happened to him, hasn't it? That's why you don't want to talk to me. 'Well, I won't move until you do tell me!'

Another pause, then the man glanced towards the African guard and nodded.

'You'd better come through,' he clipped, looking anything but welcoming. 'Tell your driver to wait. You'll not be here long.'

Kim did so, trembling with suppressed anger and distress. There was something very wrong here. All her senses told her so. And this man had the nerve to imagine that she would be content with anything but the truth!

He watched her duck beneath the barrier and walk towards him, a slender young woman with long auburn hair drawn back from a face which was striking rather than pretty, the cheekbones prominent beneath a pair of green eyes which looked right back at him without flinching.

'We'll go up to the office,' he said on a hard note,

and opened the car door.

The springs went down as he got in beside her. Kim sat silently as he turned the vehicle in a tight circle and shot back up the road again, aware of the strength in the brown hands holding the wheel. This Dave Nelson was a type of man she had not met with before, and she didn't regret that lack. No more than the early thirties, she would say, yet hard, cynical and probably quite ruthless, from the look of him. A man who had done everything, seen everything, and been impressed by none of it. A man she wouldn't trust an inch under any circumstances.

He brought the car to a halt outside one building distinguished from the others only by a chipped red door. Kim followed him into a bare, overheated room containing a couple of iron desks and filing cabinets, several plain chairs and in one corner a camp bed covered by a worn grey blanket.

'You'd better sit down,' he invited brusquely. He leaned his weight against a corner of the nearest desk and took out a packet of cigarettes from his back pocket. 'Smoke?'

Kim shook her head, making no attempt to take the chair he had indicated. She had a feeling that he was deliberately keeping her waiting as he flared a match to his own cigarette.

'You were going to tell me about Chris,' she said pointedly, and thrust both hands into the pockets of her slacks to conceal their lack of steadiness. 'Why did he leave his job?'

'Because I kicked him off the site,' was the hard reply. Grey eyes studied her clinically. 'He's living down in Freetown, if you're still interested.'

'Why shouldn't I be still interested?' she demanded. 'He might have had differences with you, but that doesn't make him a bad lot in my eyes.' She made an effort to control her voice which had risen slightly over the last few words. 'If it's not too much to ask, might I have his present address?'

Dave Nelson transferred his gaze from her face to the glowing tip of his cigarette without change of expression. 'Don't you want to know why I kicked him out?'

Kim did, desperately, but nothing on earth would have made her admit it to this man. 'I'll ask *him* when I see him,' she said. 'Now may I have that address?'

He shrugged. 'Have it your own way.' Straightening, he reached behind the desk and opened a drawer, extracted a notebook and tore out a page. 'Here.'

She took it from him, glanced at the scrawled words and then back at him. 'Did he leave this with you?'

'Not by design. I took the trouble to find out for myself.'

'Why?'

His mouth tautened visibly. 'That's my business. Have you come far?'

'England,' she answered, and saw his expression undergo a swift alteration.

'The tenacious type! Some distance to come chasing after a man, wouldn't you say?'

Green eyes sparked. 'Not when the man in question happens to be the one I'm going to marry. I don't know what happened here, and I don't want to know *your* version, Mr Nelson. But one thing I

9

do know is that Chris must have a good reason for not answering my letters.' She paused as a thought struck her. 'Providing he's even been getting them passed on.'

There was an element of calculation in the look Dave Nelson was giving her. 'Tenacity *and* faith,' he murmured. 'Quite a girl! I hope you still think he's worth it when you do catch up with him.' He reached into the drawer again and came out with a bundle of letters held together by an elastic band. 'These must be yours.'

She snatched them from him, riffled through them and looked at him gloweringly. 'They haven't been opened. Obviously Chris never even saw these!'

'He's seen them.' The answer was steady. 'He didn't bother to open them.'

That drew her up short. She stared at him blankly, her mind searching for some adequate response.

'You're lying,' she got out at last.

His brows lifted cynically. 'I am?'

'You have to be. Chris wouldn't act that way!' Her fists were clenched, the nails cutting sharply into her palms. 'You're trying to tell me that I don't know my own fiancé?'

'You might have known the man who left you behind in England,' he returned. 'That was more than eighteen months ago. The tropics does things to a man.'

'What is *that* supposed to mean?'

His lips twisted. 'How old are you?'

'Twenty-three.' The reply was drawn from her. 'And I don't see what . . .'

10

'Old enough not to need it spelling out for you,' he went on as if she hadn't spoken. 'It means that some basic urges take on rather more urgency than usual, you might say.'

Kim felt the colour rise sharply and swiftly in her cheeks. 'Now I *know* you're lying,' she retorted heatedly. 'Chris isn't ... he wouldn't ...'

'Wouldn't think of having another woman with you waiting back home—is that what you're trying to say?' There was cruelty in the line of his mouth. 'Either you're grossly over-confident or incredibly naïve!' His head jerked back as her hand came up in an arc aimed wildly at his face, and one hand shot out to grasp her wrist, pulling her off balance so that she fell against him. 'Don't do that unless you're ready to take it back,' he clipped roughly. 'You're not in England now.'

'Take your hands off me!' She pushed herself away from him, eyes blazing, face aflame. 'You obviously judge all others by your own inclinations, Mr Nelson, but you won't get me to believe what you just said about Chris!'

'You need concrete evidence? All right, go to that address and you'll find it.' His voice was hard. 'Face up to facts, sweetheart. You've come thousands of miles on a wild goose chase. That man of yours is living with another woman down in Freetown and doesn't intend giving her up. Write him off as a regular louse and go home. You shouldn't have much difficulty in finding a substitute.'

Kim's colour had faded, leaving her pale and shaken. 'Was it *your* woman he took?' she queried bitingly. 'Is that why you fired him?'

The grey eyes were suddenly dangerous. 'If it

had been I'd have done more than just that,' he said softly. 'Beginning to change your mind, are you?'

'No!' She bit her lip, sensing his derision. 'At least, I won't believe it until Chris tells me himself that it's true.'

'Then you know where to go.' He moved abruptly. 'Come on, I'll see you down to the gate.'

'Don't bother, I'll walk.'

'Like hell you will!' He was at the door before her, blocking the way out. 'I've got men out there who haven't seen anything like you in God knows how long. I aim to keep it that way. I have enough trouble keeping a full team without reminding them what they're missing stuck out here.' He opened the door, inclined his head in the direction of the Land-Rover. 'You can get in or I can put you in. Please yourself.'

Kim was trembling with anger, and some other emotion she couldn't quite put her finger on. 'Quite the tough guy, aren't you?' she said with sarcasm. 'It's easy to see that *you've* been deprived of civilised company for a long time, Mr Nelson!'

'You're right.' He said it without particular expression. 'Which makes me even less of a gentleman than I started out. Try needling me some more and you might find out how much less. Are you going to get in the car?'

Kim walked past him without another word and slid into the seat, sitting rigidly in her corner as they set off again for the main gates. So far her mind felt almost completely numb. Perhaps that was a mercy. She didn't want to start thinking just yet— not until she was far away from this place and this man. As far away as possible!

A moment later she was staring in something like horror at the empty space where her taxi had stood some little time ago, leaping from the car to run forward and gaze down the road twisting away round the shoulder of the mountain as if she expected to conjure up the other vehicle again by sheer will power.

'I told him to wait,' she said out loud. 'I told him to wait!'

Dave Nelson was having a word with the gate guard. Now he turned back to her, shrugging the broad shoulders.

'Apparently you didn't tell him firmly enough. He left almost immediately we were out of sight. Did you pay him before you left town?'

'Yes. He insisted on it.' Kim leaned weakly against the barrier, totally at a loss for what to do or say next. 'It looks as though I'm going to have to beg a lift down in your transport,' she managed at last, though it went against the grain to have to say it. She forced herself to meet his eyes. 'I'm sorry if it's against any rules.'

'It isn't.' He sounded totally unmoved by any kind of sympathy for her predicament. 'We just don't happen to have anything going through before tomorrow.'

'Oh, I'll bet you haven't!' The anger was mounting again, switching on automatically almost like a defence mechanism. 'If you think I'm going to spend a night in this ... this Godforsaken place, you've got another think coming!'

'You don't have much of a choice,' he returned. 'Unless you'd rather spend it out on the plateau.

And don't run away with the idea that I'm exactly jumping with joy at the prospect either.'

'Oh, yes, your men.' Sarcasm coloured her tone heavily. 'How are you going to keep me under cover till morning, Mr Nelson?'

'I could always hide you under my bed.' Mockery curled his lips as she flushed. 'Not quite as confident as we make out, are we? Don't worry, I've no designs on your time. I prefer my women to know the facts of life.' He ignored her indrawn lip and nodded towards the car again. 'It will have to be the club. That's about the only other place I'm likely to find you a decent bed.' The grey gaze went over her with deliberation. 'Just try to remember that our particular breed of engineer never went to public school and act accordingly, will you? I'm not saying that you're liable to find yourself seriously at risk, just that a wriggle of your hips in the wrong direction could land you in the sort of situation you'd do best to avoid.'

'I do not wriggle my hips!' she exclaimed furiously, and immediately felt a complete fool as his lips widened again. She got back into the car in seething silence, aware that a contemptuous silence would have been far more effective in the first place.

This time he took the road branching off to the left of the gatehouse, sweeping round the corner of the adjoining hill and down between overhanging trees into a cleared area containing several brick-built buildings. The clubhouse was the long low one towards the rear. There were several men lounging about in rattan chairs scattered over the sparse grass in front of it—most of them, Kim was quick

14

to note, with glasses to hand. There was a kind of semi-stunned pause in conversation when she slid awkwardly out of her seat in front of them, then a long, low whistle from off to one side which raised the flags in her cheeks again despite herself.

'Can it,' said Dave brusquely to the man who had whistled as he came round the car to join her. 'Seen Luke recently?'

'Sure, he's inside.' The other hadn't taken his eyes off Kim for a minute. 'How about introducing the visitor?'

'Later.' Dave took Kim's arm under the elbow and propelled her over the grass towards the door, ignoring the rest of the onlookers. It wasn't noticeably cooler inside, and there was a smell in the air reminiscent of the steamed jam puddings Kim could remember from her schooldays. The door opened straight into what appeared to be a recreation area, with a billiard table taking up a good half of the room. The man playing a solitary game there took a careful sighting along his cue without looking up at their entrance, put the blue into the pocket with some dexterity and straightened with a satisfied exclamation.

'It's all in the elbow,' he announced. 'If . . .' He broke off, his eyebrows shooting up, his mouth still shaped for what he had been about to say. A pair of bright blue eyes went over Kim from head to toe and back again, and his lips widened into an appreciative smile. 'So Santa did get my letter!'

Dave slung the slouch hat on to a nearby chair and ran a hand through thick dark hair. He was grinning. 'Don't count on it. Is there a room going for the lady, Luke? She'll be staying overnight.'

'Brave lass.' There was humour in the granite-like features. 'Package holiday, is it?' this time addressing Kim directly. 'I'd ask for my money back if I were you.'

'I forgot to take out the proper insurance,' she returned, smiling back involuntarily at this man who looked almost ridiculously friendly after an hour in Dave Nelson's company. 'Sorry if I'm putting anybody out.'

'Far from it. You're as welcome as flowers in May.' He laid down the cue and moved round the table towards them, stopping at the near corner to lean a hip and give Dave an inquiring look. 'Do your duty, man—or is it a secret?'

'Luke Drummond—Kimberley Freeman.' supplied the other imperturbably. 'That's all you need to know. About that room . . .'

'All right, I get the message.' The other held up a resigned hand. 'You always were a close devil, Dave.'

'I'm here,' Kim said with deliberation, 'to see my fiancé, Chris Adams.' She saw the swift change of expression with a sinking sensation, recognising in the glance he sent Dave at her side the fading of her last faint hopes that the latter had not given her the truth about Chris.

'Yes, well, we'll see about that room,' said Luke after a brief, uncomfortable moment. He turned away in the direction of a corridor leading off into the back regions. 'This way.'

'Satisfied?' asked Dave softly as Kim made to move after him, and she stiffened, pausing there with her head raised defiantly, eyes facing front.

'Not as easily as that,' she said. 'Not just because

16

you say so.'

'Luke would tell you the same story, if you asked him.'

'I daresay,' she retorted. 'I daresay they'd all tell the same story if I cared to ask them.' She made herself look at him then, jaw set against any betraying quiver. 'I doubt if there's one man here who'd risk going against anything you said, Mr Nelson. It would probably be more than his job was worth!'

A muscle jerked abruptly in his cheek just below the bone as his teeth came together. For a long, pulsating moment he stood there eyeing her narrowly before saying in rock hard tones, 'I'll say one thing for you. You've got guts. It's a pity you can't conjure up a little sense to go with them. I'm going to say it once more, and it's the last time. Don't run away with the notion that being female gives you any special immunity where I'm concerned. I'd knock a man down for saying what you just said, but there are other ways of dealing with a woman —and you wouldn't like any of them.'

Her lower lip caught between her teeth, Kim turned on her heel and went after Luke, coming on him halfway down the corridor outside the door of a small but surprisingly comfortably furnished bedroom overlooking the ravine dropping away to the west.

'Kept for the occasional VIP,' he informed her from the doorway, watching her move from window to bed to gingerly test the springing. 'Not exactly luxury class, all the same, I'm afraid.'

'Good enough for me,' she assured him. 'I shall only have it the one night. Have you worked here at the mine very long, Mr Drummond?'

17

'A couple of years. One more to go and then my long leave's due.' He leaned against the door-jamb, arms folded across his barrel-like chest. 'Six months in England, then back here for another tour.'

'Don't you find this climate a bit over-powering?'

He lifted massive shoulders. 'Sure. Most of the time it stinks. The money's good.'

Kim hesitated. 'Are you married?'

A grin split his features. 'Not on your life! Never met a woman yet that I'd trust to sit out three years at a time waiting for her man to come home.'

'Perhaps you just never met the right ones,' she returned mildly. 'There are a few around.'

'No offence.' He sounded uncomfortable again. 'I'll send somebody along to make up the bed for you. If you come through to the billiard room about five I'll see you get some food—unless you're hungry now?'

She shook her head, watched him turn to go and knew that she couldn't just leave it like this. She had to know more. 'Luke.' The name came out without thinking about it, urgently. 'What do you know about Chris yourself?'

He paused with his hand on the doorknob, looked back at her and made a noncommittal movement of his shoulders. 'Ask Dave. He knows all the details.'

'I'm asking *you*.' She was pale but determined. 'I need confirmation from some other source before I'll believe anything he tells me.'

Luke studied her curiously. 'Why should he lie about it? There's no motive for him to lie. So far as

I know he tried more than once to make Adams see sense before the whole thing blew up in his face.'

Kim wound her hands tightly in her lap. 'What happened?' she asked low-toned. 'Please tell me what happened, Luke.'

His hesitation was obvious. He didn't want to talk about it, but she had put him in a position where he could hardly refuse. 'There's nothing much to tell.' he said at last with reluctance. 'There was a fight between Adams and another man over this woman he'd got himself involved with, and the other man finished up in dock with a a couple of busted ribs.'

'But he didn't lose his job?'

'No.'

Kim swallowed painfully. 'Leaving the other matter aside for the moment. do you think that was fair?'

Again came the shrug, the look of embarrassment. 'Sure, I'd say it was fair enough, seeing that he'd lost out with Mai.'

'Mai?' Her throat felt suddenly tight as a drum. She could feel him looking at her, sense the dawning comprehension in his eyes.

'You didn't know it was one of the Creole women from the village that Adams ran off with? I thought Dave had told you that much.'

'No, he didn't mention that fact.' Kim attempted to rationalise her emotions. So the woman was an Indian, a half-caste. What difference did it make *what* she was? Chris had chosen her in preference to the fiancée waiting back in England, had gone off with her apparently without regret to live with her in a strange town, a strange country. No, not so

19

strange to him, of course. He had had almost two years of it. The hurt was beginning to make itself felt now, curling into every part of her body. How could he have changed so much, the man she had believed she knew so well? How could he have done a thing like this to her, leaving her to imagine all sorts of terrible things as the silence stretched from days into weeks?

She didn't hear the door close softly behind Luke as she sat there looking back down the time she had known Chris. He had been twenty-five to her twenty when they had first met, and they had been drawn together almost at once by the discovery that they were both of them alone in the world. Love had grown slowly between them, never the all-consuming fire one read about in some novels, but real and true all the same. At least, she had believed so. Kim could recall the day when Chris had told her about this job in Sierra Leone, the enthusiasm with which he had listed all the advantages in snapping up the opportunity to make some real money for their future together, even though it did mean postponing their marriage for three years. True, they had considered the idea of getting married anyway before he came out here, but they had both agreed that it was better to wait.

Or had *she* been the one to do the agreeing? Kim found herself wondering now. Wasn't it Chris himself who had thought up most of the arguments against leaving her a grass widow for so long?

The time had gone so slowly. Chris had written regularly, but it hadn't been enough. It was about six months ago that she had tentatively suggested coming out here to West Africa herself and finding a job in Freetown so that they could get married now instead of waiting until Chris's job finished. His reply had been swift and definite. The climate was not one to endure unless forced to do so, and she would be a lot worse off living alone in Freetown while he was stuck out at a site over a hundred miles away in the mountains. They were already almost halfway through the three years, he had pointed out, and the rest of the time would go faster. Much as he longed to see her again he did feel that any such move as she was suggesting would hardly be in either of their best interests.

It was after that that his letters had seemed to change a little, to lose something of their former cheerfulness and become somehow evasive. Kim had sensed trouble of some kind, although he had denied it emphatically when she asked him if anything was wrong. And then had come the long pause, the sudden stopping of his letters, the worry and concern. Kim had stuck it out for seven weeks before giving way to the need which had brought her halfway across the world in pursuit of an explanation. To find ... this.

She shook herself mentally. All right, so it had to be faced. The question was, what was she going to do about it? One thing was certain, she had to see Chris, to hear him tell her finally and definitely that he didn't want her. Until then she refused to believe it. The tropics did things to a man, Dave Nelson had said. Well, fair enough, that much she would accept. But she would never forgive herself if she simply left it at that.

There was a handbasin in one corner of the room. Kim made the best use of it that she could under the circumstances. With fresh lipstick and her hair combed through. she felt ready to face the world again, although the thought of seeing Dave Nelson was almost enough to make her decide to stay in her room.

She was relieved to see Luke Drummond among the men gathered in the billiard room, and even more so to find that Dave Nelson was not one of the company. Luke introduced her round quickly and succinctly without offering any particular explanation of her presence on the mine. In point of fact, no one seemed very interested in that aspect of the matter. Miracles, it appeared, were accepted wholly on face value.

Nationalities, Kim found, were many and varied, with most of the Europeans English. Senior Africans could use the club, and relations seemed amicable enough on the surface, although Chris had mentioned in his letters that things were not always so easy between the races.

By five-thirty Dave still had not put in an appearance. Neither had his name been mentioned. Kim sat with Luke and two other men at one of the tables in the dining room and ate an indifferent meal of coarse beef and stringy cabbage followed by steamed pudding and custard. Surprisingly, the coffee which ended the meal turned out to be excellent. Afterwards Luke invited her through to the bar for a drink, where she soon found herself the centre of attention again. Kim didn't mind the good-natured ribaldry. These men were tough, perhaps in some ways a little rough, but they meant no harm. Some of them hadn't seen their own countries in years, and declared they wouldn't go back under any circumstances, preferring to work their way around in jobs like this one. Others spoke reminiscently of home and family, and climates considerably kinder on the health. It was as if Kim's presence had undone a closed door for these latter, unleashed an element of homesickness they had managed to shut out until then.

Just how the fight began she wasn't quite certain. One of the Germans was leaning on the table at her side talking about a part of the Rhine Valley which they had both visited, when one of her own countrymen suddenly walked across and tapped him on the shoulder, then punched him on the point of the jaw as he turned. Next minute both men were rolling on the floor with fists flailing, while the rest were on their feet and cheering them on, offering encouragement and advice to whichever of the opponents appeared to be getting the worst of it.

In the general mêlée Luke's shouted orders went largely unheard and wholly ignored. It took the sudden appearance of Dave Nelson in the far doorway to have any effect at all on the clamour, and even then he had to shoulder his way through the press to take the warring elements by the scruff of their necks and haul the two of them bodily to their feet before any kind of real order could truthfully be said to be restored.

'What's the beef?' he demanded. 'And why in here? There's a whole mountainside you can kill each other on if you want, but I'll not have brawling in the club!'

It was the Englishman who answered him, voice too gruff for Kim to make out what he was saying, although the gesture in her direction was more than eloquent. Dave turned a hard glance on her, said a few low but apparently meaningful words to both men, then inclined his head towards the door.

'The shift's due to change in fifteen minutes. Go and put your heads under a shower and cool off. Any more trouble and I'll dock you both a month's pay.'

The men went a trifle sheepishly, followed by several more who seemed to think it might be a good idea. Dave came over to where Kim still sat at the table by the bar, hands thrust into the pockets of casual fawn slacks, face set and unsmiling.

'It didn't take you long, did it?' he said.

'I didn't do anything,' she replied with some alacrity.

'You were here, and paying attention to one man out of many. I warned you about that.'

'You didn't warn me about merely talking to them,' she came back, refusing to be intimidated. 'Can I help it if one man seizes on an excuse to take it out on somebody he doesn't like?'

'Those two,' was the brittle reply, 'are usually the best of friends. It's always the same. Let a woman run loose and there'll always be trouble! My own fault. I should have put you somewhere out of sight until I can get you out of here.'

'Well, it's nice to know you take *some* of the blame on your own shoulders,' Kim retorted, quelling any inclination to retreat. 'Shall I wear a sack over my head for the rest of the evening?'

Surprisingly his lips twitched, and a gleam of something approaching humour came into his eyes. 'No,' he said. 'The damage is already done. What

)

one

Kim
but daren
went with a ma

Luke got to his feet.
job myself,' he announced. 'Still clear outside?'

'Looked as though it might be building up for something in the north before dark.' Dave didn't sound concerned. In this part of the world they must be used to working in wet weather, thought Kim, recalling her geography from school. So far as she could remember, the average rainfall here was something over one hundred and forty inches a year, with most of that falling between May and October. Not, as Chris had said, a particularly good climate in which to live and work. Depression swamped her senses again, and she made a conscious effort to put all thoughts of tomorrow away until the time should come. No matter how much she worked round the problem nothing at all could be done about it before then.

'Another drink?' asked Dave when Luke had departed. He glanced at her glass. 'What was it?'

'Lime juice with gin in it,' she returned steadily.

'A week in this place and you'd be forgetting the lime. Are you going to have one with me, or don't I rate that much?'

'You mean you have doubts?' She lifted her brows at him, wondering a little at her own temerity in daring to taunt a man like this, yet still mindful of that gleam of unexpected humour. 'Certainly I'll have a drink with you, Mr Nelson.'

'Dave,' he said. He gave an order to one of the

the
on she
s think to
alone?' he asked.
said. 'I've been on my
own since I was eighteen.'

'Apart from Adams.'

'Apart from Chris for a year, yes.' She gave him a level glance. 'I'd prefer not to talk about it, if you don't mind.'

'I don't mind at all. I thought you might need to unload.'

'Not to you,' she answered sharply, and was immediately sorry. He seemed to be making an effort to act like a human being tonight. Why couldn't she just go along with that and leave her personal feelings about him out of it? 'I mean,' she added on a husky note, 'that you're too involved to be objective about anything, and I don't think it's fair to Chris to listen to anything else against him before hearing what he has to say himself.'

'Fair?' He gave a short laugh. 'Isn't that taking tolerance a bit far?'

Kim made a movement of her shoulders. 'You said yourself that things happened to people out here that wouldn't happen back home. Chris may have . . .'

'Not may have,' he interrupted hardily. 'Has. Okay, a man might fancy a woman to fulfil a need now and then, but he doesn't have to shack up with one like Adams has.'

'What other choice did you give him?' she demanded. 'It was you who threw him off the site.'

'Only after he'd refused to give the woman up. As it is, it's to be hoped that her husband and brothers never find out where they are.'

Momentatily Kim closed her eyes. It was getting worse, not better. 'I don't want to talk about it,' she said.

'You mean you don't want to face up to it. You're still hanging on to the hope that somehow the whole story has got twisted, aren't you?' His voice was cool and deliberate. 'Well, I can tell you it hasn't, and you're going to achieve nothing by going down there tomorrow except to cut yourself up even more. Why can't you simply cut your losses and go home?'

'Shut up!' Her own voice was low and ragged. 'It doesn't have anything to do with you.'

'I wish I could think the same way. Did you ever consider writing to the mine for information about your fiancé, or have you always given way to impulse like this?'

He was reading her pretty accurately, but Kim refused to give him the satisfaction of knowing that he had hit the nail right on the head. She *was* impulsive; she always had been. Had it been left to her she would have married Chris within a few days of meeting him because she had felt that he was a man she could be happy with. Chris had been infinitely more cautious, testing their relationship, discovering mutual interests, spending time with her before making any move to lay the foundations for a deeper involvement. That was why she found it so difficult now to countenance this new Chris, the one who had thrown away everything for the sake of . . . Sake of what? Love? Desire? That was

27

what she had to find out.

'What makes you think I'd have been satisfied to accept what I read in a letter?' she asked tautly. 'I'd still have come out if you'd given me the same story.'

'Will you get it through your head that this isn't just a story!' he said through his teeth. 'God, I've known some women in my time...'

'I'm sure you have,' she cut in recklessly. 'But it doesn't make you an expert on what makes us tick.'

'No?' He said it softly, meaningfully. 'Well, we'll see if I've got your measure tomorrow, shall we?'

Kim gazed at him for a long moment, held by the sheer force of his regard. 'Tomorrow?'

'I'll be running you down into Freetown myself, and coming with you to find your errant knight. If there's one thing I do like it's to have my theories proved.'

Heart beating suddenly and painfully faster, she said thickly, 'I don't want you with me when I see Chris—or at any other time, if it comes to that.'

'Too bad.' He pushed himself up from the chair. 'I'll have breakfast sent to your room at six-thirty, and we'll get off at seven. Do you want to finish that drink now, or take it with you?'

She was cautious. 'Where?'

'Bed.' He smiled jeeringly at the change of expression in her eyes. 'Not mine, yours. I've got to go out again, and I'm not leaving you here to spark off another incident like the last.'

'It's barely eight o'clock,' she pointed out.

'So it's barely eight o'clock. Collect some magazines from the club room as you're passing and do some reading—or you can sit and twiddle your thumbs, if you prefer it. Either way, you're not staying in here on your own. Right?'

There was very little else Kim could do but as he said, except invite humiliation by being hoisted out of the place. She hadn't known Dave Nelson very long, and she didn't want to know him for very much longer, but one thing she had learned was that he was unlikely to give any consideration to her sensibilities when it came to getting his own way. She left the glass where it was and got to her feet, conscious of the attention the pair of them were drawing as they walked together across to the door. If she was any judge at all of this particular company her reputation was going to be in shreds before morning anyway.

Dave left her at the door of the room she had been allocated, apparently not trusting her to go there under her own steam. Kim refrained with an effort from asking satirically if he would like to lock her in. He was more than capable of taking any such suggestion on its merits. Safely inside, she wandered restlessly across to the window. There was nothing much to see, of course, only the reflected glow from the arc lights illuminating the site itself and the dark wall of trees falling away towards the ravine. The muted clamour of machinery pulsed through the night, transformed by only a little stretching of the imagination into the beat of drums out there in the jungle. Home, the ordered daily routine of going to the office, the long, lonely evenings, it all seemed a million miles away. This was Africa, hot, humid and dangerously unpredictable in its effect on human emotions. She should never have come here, she told herself hollowly. Dave was right about that. Already, deep down inside, she felt different, and it wasn't a difference she liked.

CHAPTER TWO

THE anticipated rain came with a vengeance just after midnight, sounding like a hail of machine-gun bullets against the tin roof of the clubhouse. Kim lay in a bath of perspiration, unable to sleep. She had put calomine on the rash at her waist before dinner, and it had helped a lot, but now the irritation started up again so that she was forced to get out of bed and apply more of the lotion. No other sound penetrated the blanketing roar of the rain. Alone in the little room she felt isolated and vulnerable, although her door was securely locked against any possible intruders. Eventually, exhausted, she fell into a fitful sleep which took her through to first light.

Breakfast came as promised at six-thirty. By seven when she was ready to leave her room, the sun was dragging the moisture from the earth through wisps of hot mist and the temperature was already climbing into the upper seventies. Conscious of the travel-weary appearance of her shirt and slacks after a day's wear, Kim made her way out to where Dave waited for her in the club room, returning his brief greeting with a cool nod of her own.

The Land-Rover stood outside as before, only this time there were no onlookers as Kim slid into her seat. Dave didn't speak as he put the vehicle into gear and pulled away along the track leading back to the main gate. In the pale slacks and casual cotton sweater he looked somehow out of place in this setting, like a man in mufti on an Army camp. Yet Kim had the feeling that he would stand out in Freetown in exactly the same way. A man like Dave Nelson fitted his own personal category and no other.

He stopped for a couple of minutes at the gate to have a few words with the guard on duty, leaving her sitting in the car. Then he was back, and they were through the gate and heading down the mountain road towards the pass at the head of the ravine. Kim jumped involuntarily as the sharp boom of an explosion rent the air behind them, but Dave didn't turn a hair.

'We've started blasting again,' he offered in explanation. 'It's the quickest way to expose the ore.' He glanced her way, face inscrutable. 'Still of the same mind?'

'Of course.' She said it with more certainty than she felt. Now that the time was drawing near she was beginning to wish that she had simply asked to be dropped off at her hotel, leaving him with the impression that she would be going back home at the earliest opportunity. She had a strong feeling that he would insist on waiting until she had seen Chris, even if it was only to say I told you so— which meant that she would probably have to admit to the rest of it. She shook herself mentally. She hadn't even seen Chris yet, much less heard his own version of the tale. Until then she would make no plans.

The journey down to Freetown took a great deal

less time than coming up in the ancient taxi, dropping from the rough terrain of the interior plateau to the palm plantations of the lowlands. Occasionally they passed a village, standing back in the shade of mangoes, clusters of little houses with gables and fretted screens. In each one there seemed to be the same tiny church, built of rosy brick in Gothic style with windows of blue or red coloured glass, the whole smothered in bougainvillea. And everywhere the encroaching vegetation, like a green tide waiting to sweep in and cover everything in its path. Then there was the majestic sweep of the harbour ahead, and the sea of roofs nestling at the base of the mountain range stretching away to the south which gave the peninsula its name.

The town itself was brilliant and colourful, its streets thronged with traffic, its humidity overpowering. Dave eventually brought the car to a stop in a narrow side street running up from the waterfront where the overhanging upper stories of the concrete and timber houses were only feet apart.

'This is it, till the money runs out,' he said on a note of cynicism. 'And that won't be long in this part of the world.' He leaned across and opened her door. 'I'll take you in. Otherwise you'll not get past Mai.'

Kim slipped from her seat with suddenly trembling legs, almost wishing that she had taken his advice and left this whole situation alone. A group of coloured children playing in the dust stared at them with unashamed curiosity as they walked across to one of the houses. Kim smiled back at them a little uncertainly, and was rewarded with sugar-white grins in return. Then Dave was opening the peeling door of the house without bothering to knock, and ushering her into a dim passage filled with some strange, spicy smell.

A young woman appeared without warning at the far end of the passage and stood there staring at them, hands on smoothly curving hips. She was about twenty-five, with the high cheekbones and slanted eyes of the typical Creole beauty. Gold hoops glittered in her ears and about her wrists, and a gold-studded belt drew in the tight waist of her flame-coloured dress.

'Why you come here again?' she demanded in English, her eyes flashing hotly at Dave before returning to their somewhat insolent appraisal of Kim's slender figure. 'And why you bring this woman?'

'Where is he?' he said, ignoring both questions.

'Not here. Go away!' Her voice had risen, her whole body tautened. 'You come to make more trouble for Chrees. Always when you come there is trouble for Chrees!'

'He hasn't even started with trouble yet.' Dave moved forward. 'Where is he? Upstairs?'

'You not go up there!' She put herself in his way, blocking the foot of the staircase Kim could see angling upwards behind her. 'He not want to see you!'

'I don't particularly want to see him,' was the unmoved reply. 'But this lady does. Are you going to fetch him down, or shall I?'

'Mai?' The voice came from above. 'Mai, what is it? Who's there?'

Dave lifted his own voice. 'It's me—Dave Nelson. I've got your fiancée down here with me. Are you coming down, or shall I bring her up?'

There was a long pause. Kim stood motionless against the drab brown wall, hating Dave for the way he had announced her presence, hating herself for having come here in the first place, hating this whole sordid business with everything that was in her. A movement at the top of the stairs, and a man came slowly into view, ducking his head to avoid the low beam. The last time she had seen Chris he had been wearing a well-cut suit and his hair had been fashionably styled. At first glance the man who faced her now bore little resemblance to that memory. He was clad in a pair of crumpled slacks which looked as if they had been slept in, and his shirt was open to the waist. The fair hair was long and untidy, making his face look thinner, while the blue eyes she had always found so direct slid away from hers after the first stunned appraisal like rabbits running for cover.

'Hallo, Chris,' she managed to get out. 'I'm ... I'm sorry to drop on you like this.'

Dave made a sound of disgust deep in his throat, said brusquely, 'I'll wait in the car.'

There was another pause after he had gone, then Chris moved jerkily, indicating a doorway opposite to where he stood. 'You'd better come in here.'

'No!' This time it was Mai who moved, planting herself in front of the door, her face mutinous. 'She not come inside. You tell her to go, Chrees. You tell her, you hear!'

'It's all right, Mai.' His voice was cajoling. 'It's all right.' He looked back at Kim, half lifted his

35

shoulders. 'Why did you come? I told you not to come.'

'That was six months ago,' she reminded him, low-toned. 'Why do you think I came? Why couldn't you have had the courage to write and tell me yourself about . . . this?' Her voice broke a little. '*Why*, Chris?'

His mouth set and he stuck his hands into his pockets, leaning against the stairpost. 'Because I'm lily-livered when it comes to that sort of thing, I suppose. I hoped you'd have the sense to realise that I wanted out when I stopped writing. I certainly never expected you to just turn up.'

'Obviously.' She bit her lip hard. 'Can't we talk together somewhere, just the two of us? You owe me that much.'

He hesitated, caught Mai's eyes and slowly shook his head. 'It wouldn't do any good. I'm not coming back. I'm sorry it had to turn out this way, but that's the way it is. I've got everything I want right here.'

Kim drew her eyes away from the look of triumph on Mai's arrogant face with a sense of sick defeat. 'And what about the future? What are you going to do when you run out of funds?'

'I'll worry about that when the time comes. I've been earning good money these last two years.' There was unconscious cruelty in the words—or was it so unconscious? Kim wondered numbly. Maybe she had been wrong about Chris all the time. Maybe he had always been self-centred, only she hadn't allowed herself to recognise it. Whichever way, it hardly mattered now. There seemed little point in prolonging the interview further.

'All right,' she said. 'I'll go, if that's what you want.'

This time there was no hesitation. 'It would be best. You don't have to worry about me.'

'No,' she agreed on a subdued note, 'I don't think I do. Not any more. Goodbye, Chris.'

She left them both standing there in the narrow passage, and went out again quickly into the sunlight. There was a tight pain in her chest, an aching dryness in her throat. He hadn't asked how she had got here, or shown any interest at all in whether or not she could get back. So far as he was concerned she had shown total inconsideration in showing up at all. So that was that: finished: over. She was on her own.

Dave watched her cross the street towards him and climb into the seat she had vacated such a short time before. His face was impassive. 'Now where to?' he asked.

Kim moved her shoulders briefly. 'My hotel, I suppose. You don't think they'll have given my room to someone else after my being away all night?'

'It's possible. We'll have to see. There are other hotels.' He set the car into motion and drove to the corner before adding, 'Did you come by plane or boat?'

'Plane.' She gazed fixedly ahead, anticipating the next question with quivering nerves.

'There's a flight out tomorrow,' he said. 'If you've any sense you'll be on it.' Her silence drew his eyes to her, and his expression altered. 'You did book a return flight?'

She shook her head, not meeting his glance. 'I

37

only had enough for the one-way ticket. It does happen to be rather expensive to fly out here.'

'You don't say.' He sounded his horn at a dog sauntering across the street, swerved to avoid it and glanced her way again. 'Just as a matter of interest, what *are* your plans for the immediate future?'

'I don't know,' she admitted. 'I hadn't got as far as thinking about it.'

'You mean you just took off into the wide blue yonder with the one aim of finding your man or perishing in the attempt?' He shook his head. 'Like I said before, you're quite a girl, Kimberley Freeman!'

'Oh, I certainly am!' She had meant the words to sound flippant and uncaring, but her voice broke suddenly on the last and she felt the tears prickling behind her lids as reaction set in. Dave looked at her once, briefly, then turned the car into a tight gap between two buildings and bumped to a stop at the end of the blank-walled cul-de-sac.

'Okay,' he said. 'Let it go.'

Somehow, Kim found herself against his shoulder with his arm solid about her, found herself letting out the pent-up tension of the last few weeks in a storm of weeping which left her eventually spent and hicupping against his saturated shirt. Even when she recovered her senses enough to know what she was doing and who with, she didn't want to move. The arm across her back was like a barricade against the world, an armour plating against further hurt. She wanted to stay there, safe and secure.

'Try holding your breath,' he advised after a moment or two. 'It usually works.'

The sound of his voice, unmoved as ever, brought her out of it abruptly. She sat up jerkily, face flushing, eyes avoiding his, the hiccups suddenly gone. 'I'm sorry,' she said in a stiff little voice. 'I don't know what came over me.'

'Don't you?' he asked dryly. 'Well, leaving that aside for the moment, let's try and get things sorted out. How much money do you have?'

'About a hundred pounds.'

He whistled softly between his teeth. 'That won't get you far.'

'I can get a job,' she said defensively.

'Doing what?'

'I don't know. Something secretarial, I suppose.'

'You certainly had it all mapped out. You think it's as easy as that?'

She made herself shrug casually. 'Probably not. Anyway, you don't have to worry about me. If you'd just drop me off at the hotel.'

He didn't move immediately, just sat there looking at her with the air of calculation she had seen once before. 'You sure that's what you want?'

'It's a good a place as any,' she said, pride keeping her voice steady. 'I have to have a base while I'm looking for a job.'

'So you do.'

It was impossible to tell what he was thinking as he restarted the engine and backed the car out of the alleyway. Kim wondered why he had asked such a seemingly superfluous question. There was very little else she *could* do but return to the hotel for the present, although what money she had would only serve to keep her there for a few days. If she failed to find herself some kind of employment in that time . . . She put that thought firmly from her. She would just have to cross that bridge when she came to it.

The first bridge to cross came rather sooner than she had anticipated. The hotel clerk was polite but adamant. As she had not returned the night previous, they had assumed she would not be requiring her room any longer and had given it to someone else just about an hour ago. Her suitcase was to be held until Kim had paid the bill for two nights in which the room had been booked to her name.

'Pay it,' Dave advised laconically, 'and let's get out of here.' He was leaning on the desk at Kim's side, apparently quite unaware of the role which the desk clerk had so obviously allocated him in her life. Kim couldn't have agreed more about the desirability of getting out of the place fast, particularly when she saw the size of the bill for just two nights' stay. A week here and she would have been almost bankrupt.

'What now?' asked Dave when they were outside again. 'Another hotel?'

'I imagine so.' She added reluctantly, 'Do you happen to know of one a bit less expensive than this?'

'Sure,' he said. 'But not one I'd care to leave a white woman alone in.'

'It's Hobson's choice,' she came back wearily. 'I'll have to put up with the drawbacks.'

'Not the kind I was thinking of.' He looked down at her, teeth thoughtfully exploring his lower lip. 'I think a drink is called for before we go any further.'

She shook her head, impatient with his apparent

refusal to appreciate her position. 'I don't want a drink, thanks. If you won't tell me of a suitable place to stay I'll have to find one for myself.' With an air of bravado she picked up her case. 'Goodbye, Mr Nelson. Thanks for bringing me into town, anyway.'

'Hold it.' He reached out and took the case from her. 'All right, get in the car.'

Kim obeyed without argument. Pride was one thing, but at the present moment she needed his help far more. She was going to feel dreadfully alone when he did leave her, she acknowledged quiveringly. Regardless of his shortcomings, there was something in his very presence which inspired a sense of safety. While he was around nothing could happen to her.

'Whereabouts in town is this hotel you're thinking of?' she asked after a moment or two, thinking that if it was right on the outskirts of town, as seemed likely in the case of a cheaper place, then she was certainly going to have to start economising straight away by walking back to the centre to commence her job-hunting.

'What hotel?' was the reply. 'I told you we were going for a drink.'

Kim's head whipped round. 'And I told you I didn't want a drink! Stop the car and let me out. I'll find my own place!'

'You wouldn't even know where to start looking.' His expression was unrelenting. 'Anyway, I've a proposition to put to you.'

She subsided suddenly. 'Proposition? Do you mean you might know of a job I could do?'

'I might.' He spared her a glance. 'How are you

with figures?'

'Not bad. I've done a course in book-keeping.'

'Good enough.' He drew up in front of a building set back from the road which had a definite Victorian atmosphere about it. There were palms in the tiny forecourt, and a rickety wooden balcony overhanging an open veranda. A couple of Swedish-looking sailors lounged lethargically at one of the tables set along the length of the veranda. They watched Kim alight from the car with a kindling of interest which quickly dwindled again as Dave came round the front to join her.

'We can keep an eye on your case from here,' the latter commented, selecting the table nearest to the veranda steps. 'Too many light fingers in these parts.' He gave an order to the waiter dressed in white shirt, white shorts and white stockings which had turned a dingy yellow colour with age and too frequent washing, then leaned back in his seat and looked across at Kim. 'We need somebody in the wages office,' he said as if there had been no pause between this and the last comment.

Kim stared at him disconcertedly. 'Up at the mine, you mean?'

'Where else?' He added steadily, 'I'm due for home leave in about five weeks myself. The job would last till then, and the pay is good.'

Enlightenment began to dawn. 'Oh, I see,' she said. 'You mean as an employee of the Company I'd probably get a cheaper passage home?'

'Possibly. Though even with that in mind I doubt that you'd earn yourself enough in a few weeks to pay your passage to England.' His tone was dry. 'The job is for your own benefit, to give you something to do while you're stuck up there. If you travel home with me the passage will be free.'

A frown creased the space between her eyes. 'I don't see why that should make a difference.'

'It does if you're using the name Nelson.' His mouth widened satirically at the look of stunned incredulity which came over her face. 'Just a temporary measure, naturally. As soon as we got to England we'd do something about it. The main thing is that it would save a lot of trouble all round if it was legal.'

Kim's head was spinning. Marry a man she had known barely twenty-four hours? It was utterly fantastic! And yet there was a glimmer of sense from her own point of view in his reasoning. As Dave Nelson's legal wife she would have no trouble with the authorities to contend with, and it would make that job at the mine doubly secure. And it wasn't as if it would be any kind of a real marriage. He was simply offering her a way out of a situation which her own impetuosity had got her into in the first place because he felt in some way responsible for her. It just went to show how one could misjudge people on first impressions.

'I ... I don't know what to say,' she got out at last.

The grey eyes were unfathomable. 'Can you think of a better solution?'

'No,' she had to admit. 'No, I can't. It would get me home with money in my pocket, and in a reasonably short time.' She paused, met his gaze and looked quickly down at the bare wooden table top. 'I just can't see why you should be prepared to go to such lengths to get me out of a tight spot. After all, we are complete strangers.'

'We're both British,' he said sardonically. 'That has to mean something. Let's say that I can't leave a countrywoman in the lurch.' He waited a brief moment. 'Well, are you game?'

She lifted both hands, then let them drop back into her lap again. 'Like you said, there's no better solution. Certainly none that I can think of.' She hesitated, still hardly believing that he really meant it. 'When were you thinking ... I mean, how long before ...'

'What's wrong with today?' he rejoined equably.

'Today?'

'Sure.' He sounded amused. 'Getting cold feet?'

'No. No, of course not.' Kim wasn't at all certain that she was telling the truth. Today! It was all so quick. Too quick. It didn't give her time to think. Yet wasn't that best in the long run? Didn't circumstances themselves make it advisable to just go along with things? Where was the point in waiting? Her position wasn't likely to alter. Besides, it was comforting to have matters taken over like this, to have someone to lean on. Miners might be tough on the surface, but they certainly had redeeming qualities.

Their drinks had arrived. On impulse, Kim lifted her glass and smiled at the man seated opposite. 'Today,' she said. 'And I'll never make the mistake of judging anyone too harshly again.'

Just for a moment something flickered in his eyes, but it was gone before she could put a name to it. His answering smile was light and easy. 'Drink up,' he said. 'We have things to do.'

After that everything seemed to happen in a

44

kind of haze. From the bar, Dave drove down through the town again to a large, official-looking building in one of the busiest sectors. He left her alone for a few minutes in the dim outer hall, returning to find her still standing in the same position, her mind as blank as her expression. Then they were both of them in a smaller room along with some other people, and there was a great deal of talking and stamping of papers. Kim said what Dave told her to say without making sense of the words, acknowledged a smiling farewell from the man who appeared to be in charge, and found herself outside again and walking to the car at Dave's side.

'Lunch,' he said matter-of-factly. 'And then we'll get straight off. It's going to be dark before we get back, as it is.'

He took her to a café down a side street where the food was hot and spicy and plentiful, the wine throat-searing yet warmly comforting once it had gone down. Neither of them spoke very much. There didn't seem to be a great deal to say. Kim wished she had time and opportunity for a bath and a change of clothing, but it didn't appear to have occurred to Dave that such matters might be important to her right now. Neither the heat nor the humidity seemed to affect him very much. He took it in his stride, part of his job. The rainy season was due to begin any time, Kim recalled. Last night's effort had been just the prelude, the warning. She wondered what it was going to be like in the mountains when the real storms came.

Back in the car again, she sat back in her seat with a sense of detachment from reality. Not four hours ago they had arrived in the town as strangers, and now the man seated at her side was her husband. She stole a glance at the hard, lean profile, dropped her eyes to the hands resting easily on the wheel and quelled a momentary panic. This was a convenient arrangement, nothing more. There was nothing to be afraid of, nothing to worry about. Dave had made it plain from the start that she wasn't his type.

The broken night, the events of the morning, the heat and the wine she had drunk over lunch all seemed to take effect at once. Before they were five miles out of town Kim's eyelids were drooping heavily, and even the jolting of the Land-Rover on the rough surface of the road could not keep her awake. When she did open her eyes again the day was already making its swift transition into darkness, and there was a dull ache in her neck where her head had rested in an awkward position against the door frame. She sat up stiffly, putting up a hand to rub at the aching spot, met Dave's glance and felt a tremor run through as memory returned.

'Where are we?' she asked.

'About ten miles from the mine,' he answered. 'That was some sleep.'

'Yes.' She couldn't think of another thing to say. Ten miles from the mine and getting less all the time. She tried to imagine Luke's face when they walked into the clubhouse, the reactions they were bound to get from the other men. Things happened quickly in the tropics, but not *this* quickly. She wondered how many would be let in on the true state of affairs, or whether Dave would consider that nobody's business but their own. Not that anyone would be left in much doubt when it became known that they were occupying separate rooms. She supposed Dave slept in the clubhouse. Up to this moment she hadn't given it any thought. But they couldn't all of them sleep there, could they? The place wasn't big enough.

'Did I hear you mention showers last night?' she queried after another five miles had gone on the clock. 'At the moment I feel there couldn't be anything more welcome on earth.'

'You mean Luke didn't show you where they were? Lax of him.' He ran a swift eye over her as she sat there in the gloom. 'How did you cope?'

'I did the best I could with the basin. Do you live in the club?'

'No,' he said. 'All the senior engineers have houses provided. They're in a clearing the other side of the club—a regular village. There's a bathroom of sorts out at the back. It's a bit primitive, but it does the job. You might be better using the club tonight, though. It takes time to heat the water at my place.'

A house of his own. Kim wasn't quite sure how she felt about that. Right at this moment she wasn't sure how she felt about anything. The whole day had merged into one indeterminate impression, like a dream which starts to fade at the moment of wakening. The mine gates loomed up ahead, outlined against the glow from the arc lights rigged up over the site. The guard waved them through, and Dave took the narrow road down to the clubhouse, headlights cutting a swathe through the clumps of giant fern which smothered the ground between the trees. Then they were drawing up in front of the white-washed building, and Dave was reaching for her suitcase in the back.

Silence fell over the clubroom as they entered. Every eye was fixed on them, speculation rife in every face. Dave took no notice, drawing Kim with him across the room to the corridor. Behind them conversation broke out again, and there was a sudden burst of coarse laughter. Her face on fire, Kim waited until Dave stopped outside a door on the right of the corridor before saying unsteadily, 'What are you going to tell them in there?'

He turned to look at her, one hand on the door handle. 'The truth, so far as it goes. What else would I tell them?' He didn't wait for an answer, but finished turning the handle and pushed open the door. 'Lock it behind you, then you won't be disturbed. I'll go and see about some food. Come on through to the dining room when you've finished here. We'll pick your case up later.'

Kim took the suitcase from him and passed through into a longish room with shower cubicles down one side. She closed the door and turned the key in the lock as he had instructed, then moved forward to lift her case to the bench seat running down the other side of the room. Opening it, she selected a cotton print in tan and white, and hung it on a hanger from one of the hooks provided to straighten out the creases.

Fifteen minutes later, refreshed and revitalised, she came out from the shower room into the corridor again and turned left for the dining room. The clatter of cutlery ceased abruptly on her appearance. Kim directed a vague smile at the company in general, and kept her eyes fixed on Dave as

48

she made her way across the room to the table at which he was seated, conscious of his scrutiny and ironically lifted eyebrow.

'Sooner than I expected,' he commented as she took her seat opposite him. 'I ordered you a gin and lime. Okay?'

'Yes.' She took the glass and had a drink, finding it a great deal stronger than she preferred, yet hardly liking to say so. 'I wish everyone would stop looking,' she murmured uncomfortably. 'I feel like some kind of freak.'

'It's because you're not that they're doing the looking,' was the dry return. 'A woman-shaped woman with colouring like yours is very much of a rarity in these parts. The last white woman up here was an over-sized German psychologist, and she was hardly scheduled to raise anybody's temperature. Just turn a blind eye. They'll not go away, but they will become part of the background.'

'Do they all know?' she asked.

'Know what?'

'About . . .' She pulled in her lower lip, catching the gleam of derision in the grey eyes. 'You know what.'

He shrugged. 'They'll know soon enough. I don't have to stand on the table and make a formal announcement.'

Kim waited until the waiter had placed their soup in front of them and departed before adding tentatively, 'Are they going to believe it? After all, it isn't even as if I'm wearing a ring.'

'And what would it prove if you were?' He studied her a moment. 'Do you object to not having one?'

'Well,' she said defensively, 'it is more usual, isn't it?'

'Hadn't thought about it,' he admitted. 'I'll see what I can do.' He nodded towards her plate. 'Aren't you going to eat? I know it's not the Ritz, but it has its merits.'

Kim took up her spoon, smiling a little. 'I've never set foot inside the Ritz, so I've no basis for comparison. MacDonald's is more to my pocket. Do you know London at all well yourself?'

'I was born there,' he said without interest.

'Oh?' She looked at him expectantly, then as he made no attempt to add to that statement prompted hesitantly, 'Does your family still live there?'

'There isn't any family—unless you want to count an aunt in Wapping.' His lips widened briefly. 'I shouldn't imagine she bothers to count me. As it seems to be question and answer time, what happened to yours?'

'My father died when I was small, and my mother a few years ago. I was the only child. I think there's a branch of the family somewhere in Westmorland, but I've never met them. We used to have a smallholding in Kent, only it had to be sold when Dad died. So Mom went back to her job in town and I went to nursery school.' She stopped suddenly. 'Sorry, I'm going on a bit. None of that can be very interesting to you.'

Dave inclined his head noncommittally. 'I just don't believe in looking back, that's all. What's past is past. It's what's to come that matters.' A sudden mocking gleam in his eyes he raised his glass. 'Happy landings.'

It was already gone eight by the time they finished eating. When Dave asked her if she would like another drink in the bar, Kim declined, not feeling up to facing the men again at close quarters until the whole affair was out in the open and understood. She sensed rather than saw the knowing looks which followed the two of them as they left the room, and told herself resolutely that it wasn't important what they thought for now.

Her case was where she had left it in the shower room. Dave swung it easily in one hand, and led the way out to the car, greeting the men they passed en route without proffering any further remarks. By the time they reached the Land-Rover, Kim wasn't sure which she would have preferred if given a choice, the blank amazement which no doubt would greet an announcement of any kind, or this only too obvious acceptance of her status in Dave's life at present. She got into the vehicle quickly, only too eager to get away from the club and its members, eager to be alone again.

As Dave already said, the houses occupied by the senior engineers were in a large clearing just round the next bend in the track. They numbered five in all. Small, oblong buildings of brick with a narrow veranda running round three sides. This Kim managed to see in the brief moments before Dave cut the headlights and came round the car to gather her case out of the back and lead the way up the three rickety wooden steps of the second dwelling in line. An oil lamp glowed on the table set squarely in the middle of the unremarkable little living room, revealing plain teak and rattan furnishings and a couple of loaded bookshelves. A mosquito sang past Kim's face as she stood there in the doorway, landed on Dave's cheek and was promptly swatted.

'An Englishman's home is his castle,' he quoted satirically. 'Unfortunately nobody bothers to tell the livestock. Come on, I'll show you the rest of the place. Not that there's much to see.'

Another door at the rear of the room led through into a short corridor with three more doors leading off it. Dave opened the one directly opposite and motioned her through into a bedroom containing twin beds, a wardrobe and a chest of drawers. The bedcovers and mock curtains were drab green linen, the blind covering the window was made from reeds.

'I had them put up the other bed while we were having dinner,' he said. 'It makes it a bit cramped in here, but it won't be for that long.'

Kim was motionless, her eyes on the narrow space between the beds, her heart suddenly thudding into her throat. 'Are . . . are you planning to sleep in here?' she managed at last.

The pause was brief. 'Naturally,' he said evenly. 'Where else would I sleep? There's only the one bedroom.'

The eyes she turned on him were wide and dismayed. 'But you . . . can't!'

'I can't?' He regarded her with cynicism, lifting his lip. 'Is that any way for a wife to talk to her husband?'

'It isn't like that. You know it isn't!' She fought to control the rising panic inside her. 'You only married me to stop the other men from getting ideas about me while I'm here. You said it would make things easier.'

52

'So it does. All round.' There was no sign of weakening in his face. 'Come on, you weren't born yesterday. You didn't really think I'd settle for the kind of conditions you're talking about? I offered you marriage to get you out of a spot, but I never said anything about forgoing the compensations.'

'You tricked me!' At that moment it didn't sound at all ridiculous. Her face was pale. 'You deliberately led me to believe that you were only offering me a temporary way out.'

'True enough. The offer still is temporary. Five weeks here, then back to England and a quick separation.' His voice was implacable. 'Only make no mistake about it, while it does last there'll be no rules.'

Hands clenched tightly at her sides, Kim said in low tones, 'If you touch me, I'll ... I'll kill you!'

'That should make for an interesting relationship.' He moved his shoulders away from the door-jamb. 'I've got to go up on the site for an hour or so before turning in. As you're so intent on preserving your girlish ideals, I'll make sure to knock before I come in again.' He lifted a mocking hand. 'See you.'

Kim remained where she was, gazing at the closed door for several seconds after he had gone. She felt quite numb, both physically and emotionally. Where did she go from here? How did she begin to cope with the man who had just left her—a man in whom she could trace no glimpse of the qualities she had credited him with only that morning. She was married to a stranger, and a frightening stranger at that. He had meant every word he had said to her, that much was certain.

When he returned he was going to expect her to submit to him regardless of her own feelings, regardless of anything but the fact that she was legally his wife.

A tremor ran through her suddenly as the numbness began to wear off. She couldn't go through with it. She *wouldn't* go through with it! At least, not willingly. If he wanted her he was going to have to fight her every inch of the way. With deliberation she blotted out the memory of the hardness and strength of his shoulders and arms, the knowledge that fighting a man like that would be tantamount to trying to stop a bulldozer with a pedal car. Crossing to the door, she turned the key in the lock and stood with her back to it, studying the room. That chest of drawers looked heavy enough. If she could manage to drag that across the door it should be sufficient—for tonight anyway. What was going to happen after that she didn't even want to consider for the moment.

She was sitting on the bed still fully dressed when she eventually heard Dave come into the house again. There was the sound of the outer door being closed, then his footsteps coming through the living room. Fascinatedly, Kim watched the door handle depress, heard the rattle of the lock tongue. The pause seemed to last an age. She had almost begun to believe that he had gone when the jarring crash of a foot meeting the wood just below the handle brought her starting upright in dismay. Heart hammering, she sat there fixedly as the door gave with a sound of tearing wood and the chest of drawers was pushed inexorably to one side. Dave stood in the opened doorway, his breath coming a little heavily, his mouth an inflexible line.

'You don't learn very fast,' he said. 'You're not going to get out of this, green eyes, so you may as well quit trying. It's about time you started acting like a grown woman.'

'So that you can act like an animal?' She flung the words at him across the width of the room, her fear of him momentarily swamped by sheer pulsating fury. 'If a bedmate was all you wanted you could have got one without having to marry her first!' Pure instinct sent her scrambling on her knees to the far side of the bed bare seconds before he reached her. 'You lay a finger on me, and I'll yell loud enough for them to hear me down in Freetown!'

'I'm going to do a damn sight more than lay a finger on you,' he stated softly and emphatically. 'And you can scream your head off for all the good it's going to do you. What do you expect, a rescue squad at the door? You made a bargain, and you're going to stick to it!'

His lunge across the bed to grab her by the wrist was so swift that Kim had no chance to sidestep. With desperation lending her strength she fought back against him, hammering at his face with her fist without even noticing the pain herself. When that failed to make any impression she swiftly bent her head and sank her teeth into his wrist, feeling a sudden savage exultation at his sharp exclamation.

Next minute she was flat on her back on the bed and he was towering over her, eyes glinting, mouth pulling into a merciless smile, hands pinning her down into the pillows. Then his shoulders were blotting out the light, his mouth coming down on hers with a bruising demand which took the world and spun it crazily around her head.

The siren's strident wail brought sudden release. Dazedly Kim saw Dave sit up, felt his hands leave her body. His head was up, his whole demeanor changed. 'Emergency,' he said, and was on his feet even as he spoke and striding across the room. She lay motionless where he had left her as the door banged shut behind him.

CHAPTER THREE

THE sound of an engine woke Kim from the doze into which she had fallen about three o'clock, bringing her starting upright in the chair. Dawn was streaking the sky, early light filtering in through the partially opened reed blinds over the living room windows. She forced herself to remain seated as footsteps came on up on to the veranda and the door was pushed open.

Dave looked tired and grimy, his shirt open to the waist and ripped down the length of one sleeve. There was grey dust in his hair and settled into rivulets along the lines of his features, adding ten years to his age. He stood there in the doorway for a moment eyeing her, a faint smile flickering at the corners of his mouth.

'You didn't have to wait up,' he said. 'It's enough for one of us to lose a night's sleep.'

'Was it an accident?' Her voice was low but steady.

'A landslide. The rain brought a section of the undercut down. Three men trapped, but we got them out.' He moved further into the room, rubbing a hand across the back of his neck. 'What I need is a shower.'

'Without hot water?'

'Cold will do for the time being. I can always have another when I get up.'

Kim gripped the arms of her chair as he made to pass her. 'You're going back to bed? Just like that?'

He paused, turning his head to look down at her. 'Not back. I never got there, if you remember. It mightn't be a bad idea if you went yourself. The way I feel right now you've nothing to worry about. I'll sleep like a log for the next few hours.'

'Dave.' This time her voice had a slight tremor. 'We can't ... you can't simply ignore what happened last night. All right, so I misunderstood your motives. Naïve of me, perhaps, but that's the way I apparently am. Under the circumstances I think it would be best if we forgot the whole arrangement and I went back to Freetown. I'll find my own way home.'

There was little change in his expression. 'First of all, nothing did happen last night. It didn't get the chance. And the arrangement stands. I said I'd get you back to England, and I will.'

'At a price!'

He shrugged. 'You were prepared to use me; why shouldn't I expect some repayment?'

'I wasn't using you,' she protested. 'Not the way you make it sound. You made the offer.'

'Sure I did. And I'm also making the rules. You could save yourself a whole lot of bother if you accepted things as they are.'

'And you too, I suppose,' she flung back with sarcasm.

His smile was slow. 'Not particularly.' He registered the sudden increase of heat in her face with satire. 'Five weeks isn't such a long time. In fact, it could pass all too quickly. I might even keep you a bit longer than that.'

Kim jerked up her head, her eyes brilliant. 'You'll keep me just as long as it takes me to find some way of getting away from this place! And I will find a way, even if I have to walk! You won't always be around.'

'No,' he agreed, 'I won't. Only remember the rains are coming, and you'd be lucky to last more than twenty-four hours out there on your own. There also happen to be at least fifty men I can call on with tracking experience, and if I did have to come after you ...' He left it there with a sudden weary gesture. 'I'm going to find that shower. You do as you want, only don't waken me before ten unless something urgent crops up.'

It was a long time before Kim stirred from the chair. Eventually, she got up slowly and went across to snap up the blind, standing there looking out across the baked red earth of the clearing. The trees beyond were motionless, wreathed in the hot forest mist which would soon give way to the steadily mounting sun. From here the site was hidden, the noise blanked off by the intervening shoulder of the mountain. A hundred miles from civilisation, and it might as well have been a thousand. Even if she could steal a car she would never get it past the main gate.

Her jaw firmed suddenly. One thing was certain, she would not be giving Dave Nelson the opportunity to finish what he had begun last night. She would take her chances down in Freetown, if it meant stowing away in one of the mine trucks to get there. Chris must help her, she thought desperately. If he would only loan her the price of an air ticket home she would promise to send it back to him the moment she got there, if she had to go on her knees to her bank manager to do it. As to her marriage—who was to say that it was even legal in England? And if it was—well, that was something which would have to be faced. The price of impetuosity, she told herself ruefully. Perhaps this would teach her to look before she leapt in future.

A noise in the corridor brought her head round sharply. She relaxed again as a young African man appeared in the doorway, prepared to welcome anyone in preference to Dave. The newcomer was dressed in the same sort of jacket and dun-coloured trousers as worn by the waiters at the club, and carried a cloth in his hand. He stopped when he saw her, looked nonplussed for a brief moment, then flashed his teeth in a brilliant smile.

'Missis like breakfast now?'

Conscious of her crumpled appearance, Kim confusedly shook her head. 'Not just yet. Are you from the club?'

'I am Patrick,' he said. 'I work in the house for Boss Nelson.'

A position of some standing, no doubt, she thought cynically. 'All right, Patrick,' she said with an effort at normality. 'I'll have toast and coffee in about half an hour. Is . . . there anyone in the bathroom?'

He looked a little perturbed. 'No hot water yet, missis.'

'It doesn't matter. Cold will do.'

It was only as she moved past him to the door that she realised her suitcase was still in the bedroom where Dave had dropped it last night—and he was in there now. She paused, biting her lip, felt Patrick's eyes on her back and forced herself to carry on. Heart beating fast, she quietly turned the handle and pushed the door open enough to see the dark head on the pillow of the nearest bed. His face was turned away from her, his breathing deep and even. Hardly daring to breathe herself, she slipped into the room and closed the door almost to behind her, standing with her back to it while she studied the figure in the bed. He lay on his front with the sheet across his waist, his back bare and bronzed against the linen. One arm lay flung over the edge of the mattress, the hand open and hanging. Even in sleep there was a look of tremendous power in the tautly muscled body.

Her case was on the far side of the room under the window. Still holding her breath, Kim moved away from the door and across to get it, freezing with her hand already reaching out as Dave moved suddenly, rolling over on to his back with a drawn-out sigh. Only when she was quite sure that he was still unconscious did she complete her own movement, lifting the case and turning back to the door.

Despite her need to get out of the room with all haste, she found her eyes drawn inexorably to the face on the pillow, travelling over the strongly carved mouth lines beneath the thick dark hair to linger for a pulsating second or two on the ruthlessly moulded mouth. Last night those arms had held her, that mouth kissed her, and she had known then that there was no escaping either once they had claimed her. Had the siren not sounded when it did she would have been helpless against his strength and purpose; there was no getting away from that. Only the dire need of men in danger had saved her from being taken like one of the slave girls which the area had once provided in quantity, and she could hardly hope for such timely deliverance again. She had to get away today, she thought fiercely. One way or another it had to be today!

The bathroom was a small bamboo enclosure leading off the rear veranda with a roughly thatched roof and a system of rope pulleys which provided a surprisingly effective shower from an overhead tank. Drying herself was no problem, dressing in such confined space certainly was. Eventually she emerged feeling clean and refreshed in cream linen slacks and matching shirt, to fold the crumpled tan and white dress into her case. It would be safe enough out here for the time being, she decided. She wasn't sure yet how quickly she was going to need it.

The cool shower had gone a long way towards restoring her sense of balance again. What was done was done; there was no sense in dwelling on it. What she must do now was to turn all her concentration towards escape. It wouldn't be easy, she acknowledged. Chris had once mentioned that the railway waggons only went as far as Pepel on the north bank of the Sierra Leone river, and that was some miles up river from Freetown. In any case, from what she had seen of them there would be little chance of finding a place to hide in them during the journey down from the plateau. That left the road, and so far she had no idea what kind of transport was used—if any—or how frequently. The best bet seemed to be vehicles from outside. There must be deliveries some time of fresh meat and vegetables. Some time—but maybe not today, or even tomorrow. So, she promised herself resolutely, if all else failed she would bribe somebody to take her out. If she arrived on Chris's doorstep destitute he might be more prepared to help her. For the rest—Mai was welcome. Everything she had ever felt for Chris as a man had died back there in the dingy corridor yesterday.

The dining table was already laid when Kim went through to the living room. Patrick brought in chilled fruit juice and a rack of freshly made toast from the kitchen, then went back for the coffee. Questioned, he told her that he lived in the township over the ridge and had worked here at the mine since he was a boy. All the men from the town worked on the mine, accepting the inevitable much as the miners in the north of England did because there was no other work in the area. Patrick himself appeared quite happy about it. He had a wife and children, and could afford to keep them in comfort on his earnings. Kim wondered what constituted comfort to the African mind, but didn't like to pry too deeply. She would also have liked to ask how he had got his Irish name, only she suspected that the answer to that one was rather obvious. His skin was several shades lighter than most of the other Africans she had seen so far on the site.

Trying not to sound too interested in the answer, she asked him casually about supplies to the mine, to be informed that deliveries were few and far between, with the last one on the day before she had arrived. Mail and other minor items were brought in weekly by helicopter, due again today.

Kim pricked up her ears at this last. Stowing away in a helicopter might prove difficult, but there was a chance that the pilot might be persuaded to give her a lift. That would solve half her problems at one stroke. A quick trip down, and see Chris before Dave had a chance to get on her trail.

She was finishing her second cup of coffee when Luke came up the steps to the veranda. He paused in the open doorway, his gaze flicking briefly about the room before coming to rest on Kim.

'Hi,' he said. 'Dave not here?'

'He's asleep,' she answered. 'He said not to waken him before ten. Is it urgent, Luke?'

'Wouldn't gain anything to wake him up now. I just heard that one of the boys he pulled out from under the dozer died half an hour ago. Internal injuries, the doc says. Nothing he could do.'

'I'm sorry,' Kim offered in quick compassion. 'Did he have any family?'

'Yes. They'll be taken care of. He was one of our best drivers.' He shook his head. 'Dave's going to be cut up about it.'

'Losing a driver?'

Luke studied her a moment before replying. 'A bit more than that,' he said. 'Is there any of that coffee going spare?'

'It's too cool,' she answered quickly. 'I'll get Patrick to make some fresh.'

'I'll tell him.' He moved across to the rear door and directed a stentorian roar down the passage in the direction of the kitchen premises. 'Pat, coffee!' Turning back, he caught Kim's expression and grinned fleetingly. 'Don't worry, it would take more than that to disturb him. In this job you train yourself to sleep through everything but the alarm siren.' He paused. 'I hear tell you're going to work in the pay office.'

'That was the idea,' she replied carefully. She took another sip from her cup, put it down again and looked up. 'Why don't you say it, Luke?' she asked on a note of rather shaky defiance.

'Say what?'

'What you're thinking.'

He shrugged 'Wouldn't be much to tell. Getting hitched up like you did is your affair and Dave's. You could have done a lot worse. He'll see you right.'

She had made her bed and so must lie on it— that just about summed it up, she thought with irony. At any rate, it was pretty obvious that Luke would not be prepared to involve himself in helping her get away. Not that she could blame him. Nobody with any sense would tangle with Dave Nelson.

Patrick bought in the fresh coffee and another cup, offering Luke a cheerful greeting. Kim poured for him, added sugar to his taste and waited until he had drunk half of it before saying tentatively, 'Shouldn't you be resting yourself after being up all night? You must all have had a bad time of it.'

'Dave took the brunt of it. If that dozer had gone right over there would have been four dead men this morning instead of one. He got under it with props and held it up till we'd dug 'em out. He only just got out in time himself. Another minute and . . .' He left it there. 'I had an hour or so myself before Doc Selby sent the news down. After that

I'd had enough. Guess Dave will feel the same when he knows.'

'Knows what?' asked Dave from the doorway. He stood there looking in at them, an old towelling bathrobe tied about his middle, his feet bare in a pair of open leather sandals. His hair was rough and wavy at the ends, his jaw dark with several hours' growth of beard, but the grey eyes were keen. 'Knows what?' he repeated.

Luke told him in two words. Watching, Kim could detect no visible effect.

'Tough,' he said. 'That coffee fresh?'

There was a cup already on the table for him. He filled it himself, tossed off the contents and rested his gaze on Kim's face as he put it down again. 'Life's cheap round these parts,' he said on a hard note. 'You'll get used to it.'

'Not if I can help it,' she came back with emphasis.

Luke said quickly, 'Sorry if I got you up, Dave. Didn't think you'd be hearing anything for another couple of hours yet.'

'I've been awake for a while,' the other returned. 'Couldn't get back to sleep for some reason. Maybe a premonition.' He hitched up a chair and sat down, glanced towards Luke again. 'More coffee?'

'I've had all I want, thanks.' He got to his feet without haste. 'I'll be on my way. See you later.'

'It's more than likely.' Dave leaned both elbows on the table as the other man went out, holding his cup between his hands as he said casually. 'You seem to be hitting it off with Luke.'

'With him I know where I am,' she returned. 'Luke says what he means.'

'According to you I haven't been doing much beating about the bush myself,' on a dry note. 'Don't blame me because you've spent your life in cloud-cuckoo land. The kind of gallantry you're looking for went out with King Arthur's court!'

'All I'm looking for is civilised behaviour,' came the uneven retort. 'You can't even be bothered to dress before you sit down to a meal.'

His grin was taunting. 'I haven't shaved either, as you may have noticed. Ever been kissed by a man with stubble on his chin?'

She gave him a look of concentrated distaste and pushed back her chair. 'I'm sure you'll understand if I prefer the veranda.'

'Kim.' His voice was soft but with a note in it which slowed her in her tracks despite herself. 'Come back here.'

She refused to look round although her heart was thudding against her ribs. 'I said I was going outside.'

What might have happened next had Patrick not chosen that precise moment to enter the room bearing a laden plate of ham and eggs, Kim hated to think. When she turned her head Dave was subsiding back into his seat, but the gleam in his eyes spoke volumes for his intentions. It was something to hang on to, the fact that he obviously was not prepared to make an issue of anything in front of the African, although she could hardly hope to have Patrick around all the time. She seized the opportunity now to make her escape on to the veranda, sinking gratefully into one of the two rattan chairs with a feeling of having won a temporary respite only.

The other houses in the clearing appeared deserted, the only sign of movement in the heat shimmering over the ground. Even here under the comparative shade of the palm thatch covering the veranda the atmosphere was oppressive, creating instant lethargy. Kim could feel the perspiration already soaking her shirt round the waist, and was thankful that the threatened rash appeared to be making no headway. Given time, she supposed one became accustomed to regulating all movement to a slower pace during the day, to conserving energy instead of expending it. Only she wasn't going to be here long enough to find out how much time it took to learn how to live comfortably in the tropics. She had had more than enough already.

She was still sitting in the same position an hour or so later when Dave came out to join her. He was dressed in much the same manner as when she had first seen him, except that he was carrying the soft slouch hat. His jaw was smooth again.

'I'll take you up and show you the ropes,' he said easily. 'You'd better get a hat.'

Kim took hold of herself sharply. It was no use saying all the things which trembled on the tip of her tongue. It would be like water off a duck's back. In any case, it would be to her advantage to go with him in order to assess her own position with regard to transport. In that respect alone his offer couldn't have been better timed. She got up without speaking and went round the veranda to fetch the nebbed butcher's boy cap from her case. Not quite the kind of thing one normally expected to see in the tropics, she imagined, but the only one she possessed. She stuck it defiantly on the back of her head as she went back to where Dave waited for her. Stalking past him to the steps, she felt his hand come out and tip the cap forward.

'That way, so that it shields your eyes,' he said. 'Your hair will save the back of your neck.'

The accounts office was almost directly opposite the one to which Dave had taken her that first day. It was stifling inside. The four African clerks watched them surreptitiously from beneath industriously lowered lids as Dave showed her the books and files, fingers busy with piles of buff-coloured envelopes and trays of currency. The main part of her own job would be the calculation of money due to each man on the labour force from time sheets, and the making out of pay slips to be attached to the front of each envelope. All the Africans had to do then was to follow her figures. A load of responsibility, and from the look of the sample time sheet which Dave showed her, no simple task, taking into consideration the bonuses, overtime and piece-work rates which could be earned.

'All extras are paid out a week in arrears,' he explained. 'We only work the single shift Saturdays, so that the sheets are in by five. That gives you three or four clear days to get the figures out. Think you can cope?'

'Did you ever think of asking the Company for a computer?' she hedged.

'With Loxley Gunter around we've never needed one. He's got a ready reckoner inside his head.'

'I gather he left?'

Dave shook his head. 'Extended leave. Medical reasons.'

'I see.' Kim turned the page in the beautifully kept ledger, running her eye down the columns of figures. 'What would have happened if I hadn't been available?'

'The Company would have been forced to appoint a new man. This way we can probably hold out till he gets the okay to start work again. The Nigerians are a strong race. He'll get by.'

Kim didn't like to ask what was wrong with the man, and Dave didn't seem inclined to add the information. To leave the mine now would be to rob this Loxley Gunter of the chance of retaining his job in effect. But she couldn't stay on. If she did it would be on Dave's terms, and that she refused to accept. Sympathetic though she might feel towards the absent Nigerian, in this instance she had to put herself first.

A man she recognised from the club the previous evening stuck his head round the door, his glance sliding over her swiftly before going on to Dave. 'You're needed up top,' he said. 'Trouble.'

'Be right there.' Dave came away from the desk edge, reaching for his hat. 'Stay and have a browse round,' he said to Kim. 'If you do go outside steer clear of the loading bays, and don't attempt to walk back to the house. I'll be back.'

To Kim there was more threat than promise in the latter statement. She nodded without answering, keeping her eyes on the ledger in pretended absorption as he left the office. Without lifting her head more than an inch or two she watched him set off up the hill, heaving a sigh of relief when the car finally passed out of sight beyond the corner of the building. When she turned it was to find all four clerks regarding her with frank curiosity. She smiled at them awkwardly, tried to find something to say to them and could think of nothing adequate to the moment. Silently and perversely she cursed the man who had left her in this predicament.

'I ...' she began hesitantly, then stopped because every eye had swung towards the window as if at some prearranged signal. Following the direction of their gaze, Kim saw the brightly coloured fuselage of a helicopter coming in over the ridge, the wind from its whirling rotor blades flattening the treetops, the noise of its engine mingling with the general clamour of site activity. Then it was descending, passing from sight behind the tin roofs on the far side of the dirt road, the only indication of its whereabouts in the cloud of dust swirling into the air.

The Africans broke into excited comment in their own language. Obviously the weekly visit of the helicopter was quite an event in their lives. Forgotten for the moment, Kim made her way to the door and slipped out, glad to get away from the oven-like atmosphere. It was scarcely better outside, the sun a furnace which beat down through the crown of her head and seemed to penetrate her brain. The cloud of dust was settling, drifting down behind Dave's office. She crossed the road cautiously, jumping over the ruts left by some heavy vehicle after the rain and passing between two of the buildings. The helicopter lay below and to her right on a flattish piece of ground down towards the main gate. Its pilot was talking with a couple of other men a few feet away. His hair was very fair and bright in the sun. Kim felt her throat tighten, and closed her mind to the invading images. This wasn't the time to be thinking of Chris. This wasn't the time to be thinking of anything but escape from a prison of her own making.

She had to go back to the road to get down to where the machine was. She walked as quickly as she could, hugging the sparse shade of the buildings and ignoring the few people in the immediate vicinity. The pilot was dragging a sack from the interior of the helicopter as she rounded the last corner and came out into the open. He saw her approaching as he turned to hand over the sack to one of the two men, and a look of sheer surprise came over his face.

'Well, this is really something!' he exclaimed. 'Are you real, or is it a mirage I'm seeing?'

Kim smiled, noting the American accent and frank, open features. 'I'm Kimberley Freeman,' she said without hesitation. 'And I'm quite definitely real.'

'That's a relief.' He grinned, leaning back against the fuselage under the shade of the rotor shaft. 'Jerry Brice. Don't tell me they've got women working up here now!'

'All right,' she said obligingly, 'I won't.' She stuck her hands in her pockets, looking up at the gleaming metal. 'Is this yours?'

'Wish it was. I only work for the company that owns this baby. I get the bread and butter, they get the jam.'

'Oh.' She considered him for a moment. 'I thought money—big money—was the only thing that brought men to this part of the world.'

'Initially it is. Fine if you can get it, but . . .' He

paused, shrugged. 'There's something about the tropics that gets a hold on you. I've been here four years, and so far I'm not thinking of going back home. I guess after all this time I'd miss the sheer hell of it all. Are you here for long yourself?'

'Just visiting,' she answered quickly. 'As a matter of fact, I was wondering if I could beg a lift down to Freetown when you go. The road takes so long.'

'Sure. Why not?' He sounded more than agreeable. 'But only if you're ready to go now, I'm afraid. I've got a time schedule to catch up on this trip.'

Kim made up her mind quickly. If she went back for her things she would miss this chance, and if Chris was going to help her at all it might as well be all the way. 'Yes,' she said, 'I'm ready now.'

'Okay, climb in.' He pushed the sliding door back to its fullest extent and got behind the controls first, extending a hand to help her up the step. 'That's it. Just pull the door by that catch there and slide it along into the lock.' His eyes moved beyond her, and he put out a sudden hand to stay the movement. 'Hang on a minute. There's Dave Nelson coming across. Haven't seen him this last couple of trips.'

Kim whipped her head round to see the broad-shouldered figure advancing fast across the dusty stretch of bare earth, and knew a moment's pure panic. It was too late. Already he was too close. Her attempt to escape had failed before it had even properly begun. She sat there sick with defeat waiting for the man she had married to reach the machine.

His face when he did come up was hard to read.

Kim looked down into the grey eyes and couldn't decide whether the glint in them was caused by anger or amusement. The latter seemed unlikely. Not when his pride was at stake, as it had to be now. There could be no mistake about her intention, no way of getting round the fact that she had tried to use Jerry Brice in this bid to get away from him. Not even Dave could save face in a situation like this.

He didn't even try. 'Come on down,' he said hardily, and then to Jerry himself, 'Sorry to deprive you of your passenger. My wife will be staying.'

The other man's expression altered abruptly. 'Your wife?' His gaze slid to Kim confusedly. 'You said your name was Freeman.'

'I know,' she said, not meeting his eyes. 'I'm sorry.'

Dave put his hands on her waist as she turned her body to reach for the step, lifting her to the ground and holding her there in front of him, his fingers burning through her shirt. 'See you next trip,' he said to Jerry in tones which left no room for misinterpretation.

The other needed no stronger hint. A look of total confusion still on his face, he closed the door and waited until they were both clear of the machine, then brought the motor to life. Kim's hair was whipped over her face as the blades began to turn. Half blinded, she saw the helicopter begin to rise, saw Jerry looking down on them as it hovered for a few brief seconds, then it was sliding off and up towards the ridge again. Only then did Dave's hands slacken their grip, although he didn't let her go altogether.

'Try that again,' he said softly, just behind her ear, 'and you'll have something to run away from!'

Out here in the open, in daylight, she felt as safe as she was ever likely to feel with him. Safe enough, at any rate, to say the words which came bitterly to her lips. 'I already have. You can't make me stay here.'

'No?' This time he definitely was amused. 'And where were you thinking of going if I'd let you leave just now?'

'I don't know,' she lied. 'And I don't care. Anywhere away from you!'

'Liar.' He swung her about so that she was facing him, keeping her in front of him. 'You were going to see Adams again—hoping he'd have the decency to see you right. When are you going to learn that he doesn't want to know? So far as he's concerned you could walk the streets for a living.'

'Would that be so very different from what you're offering me?' she flashed, and felt every nerve in her body signal a warning as his eyes narrowed.

'I married you, remember,' he said softly. 'All legal and above board. Custom here dictates that a wife obey her husband in all matters, or suffer the consequences. I'm not against fighting with you in private, green eyes, but I'll make you remember it if you try showing me up in front of anyone else again.' He let her go, smile jeering. 'We'll have a meal at the club. I told Pat he could have the afternoon off.'

'I'm not hungry,' she said thickly. 'I'd rather just go back to the house.'

He shrugged. 'Suit yourself.'

Deposited some ten minutes later on the doorstep, Kim went straight indoors without waiting to see him turn the car and drive off again. Patrick had already left. Kim didn't blame him. The dimness of the living room was balm after the glare outside. She tossed her cap into one chair and sat down in another to flip unseeingly through one or two back-dated magazines. There was nothing here to interest her anyway. This was a man's house, a man's world. There was no real place for her.

Eventually, needing something to occupy her mind, she went out to the kitchen and heated water for coffee, finding the latter after some searching in a battered biscuit tin in one of the cupboards. There were ants in the cupboard too, she discovered. Something should certainly be done about those. First thing in the morning she would set Patrick to scrubbing them all out with insecticide, and scouring the various tins. If she had to stay in this place any length of time at all she was taking no chances with her health.

If she had to stay? Her breath caught roughly in her throat. What other choice did she have?

CHAPTER FOUR

IT was a long sultry afternoon. Kim was glad to spend the greater part of it lying on one of the beds in the bare minimum of clothing. She wondered what Patrick had thought about the smashed lock, if he had thought anything at all. Probably he accepted everything that happened in a white man's home as a matter of course, just as he had accepted her presence here this morning with scarcely a blink. In many ways she supposed it would pay her to cultivate the same attitude for the duration of her residence. There was no escaping Dave. He had her blocked at every turn. And tonight there would be nothing to stop him from claiming the rights which she herself had given him. She could fight him, but for how long? And why bother anyway when she knew she was bound to lose? There would be more dignity in a total lack of response. More dignity, and far less satisfaction for a man such as he was. If he found her unwilling to put up any kind of resistance he might even lose interest.

She took another shower at six, and changed into a plain blue tricel dress with a plaited belt. When she came into the living room Patrick was putting clean glasses out on a tray along with a couple of bottles. For the first time in her life, Kim actually felt more than ready for the drink he offered to prepare for her. She chose gin with lime, and sat with it in line with the doorway to catch the faint breeze which had sprung up since darkness had fallen. This was only the third night she had spent here, yet it seemed an age since the morning when she had left Freetown to come up here to look for Chris. Strange how the thought of her former fiancé conjured up no kind of feeling whatsoever. He was there, and she would have been ready to use him if she'd had the chance, but only because she felt nothing for him any more.

She was still only halfway down her drink when the car came down the track to draw to a halt outside the house. She stayed where she was as Dave came on up the steps, raising the glass with deliberation to her lips.

'Didn't take you long to catch the habit,' was the satirical comment. He dropped to a chair, eased off one boot and then the other and stretched out with an air of relief. 'How about fixing me one?'

Kim got to her feet without a word and crossed to the cabinet. 'What will you have?'

'Whisky—straight.' He sounded faintly surprised. Kim poured a good measure into one of the heavier based glasses and took it to him before regaining her own seat. She could feel him watching her as he drank, and took care to keep her expression blandly unaware. Nothing he could say or do was going to undermine her newly won control. She was determined on that. From now on she would be the most docile wife a man ever had, and see how he liked that. If she read him correctly he would be bored to death within twenty-four hours. The Dave Nelsons of the world never wanted what they could come by easily.

The silence stretched out, broken only by the whirring of crickets and Patrick's cheerful if tuneless whistling from the kitchen as he prepared the evening meal. When eventually Kim did steal a glance in Dave's direction he was swirling the liquid left in his glass with an enigmatic smile on his lips. The lift of his head caught her unawares. He raised the glass in her direction, drained the contents and stood up.

'Must make myself presentable. Don't have too many of those if you're not a hardened drinker. They might have an unexpected effect.'

They ate at eight, the meal filling if uninspired: steak out of a tin enlivened with spices and herbs, tinned peas and plain boiled rice, and to follow steamed fruit pudding in a lumpy yellow sauce which tasted nothing like custard. Dave ate what was put before him without comment, so the indifference of the meal was certainly nothing unusual. Kim determined to have a few words with Patrick herself in the morning. Even food out of tins could be made more palatable than this.

It was Dave who suggested taking their coffee out on the veranda. The night was black, the breeze strengthened into a fitful wind. Thunder grumbled distantly. Tonight there were lights in one of the other houses, and the sound of male voices and laughter echoing across the clearing.

'Card school,' said Dave casually. He had his feet up on the rail, his chair tipped back comfortably. 'That's Carl Gerhardt's place. Best poker player I ever met.'

'Do you usually join them?' Kim asked.

'More often than not. It passes the time.'

'Well, don't let me keep you.'

His smile was mocking. 'Leaving you on your own? They'd think I'd gone mad. There's not one of them in there who wouldn't give a year's pay to be in my shoes. You're attractive enough to draw attention wherever you are, but here you're a sensation. You'll be figuring in more dreams, waking *and* sleeping, than you could count!'

'Stop it.' Her voice was low. 'I don't want to know how I affect the men here. I'm not interested!'

'Not much. You wouldn't be normal if you didn't get a kick out of it, especially knowing that you're safe from any adventurous type who might decide that dreams weren't enough.'

'Don't you mean depraved?' she retorted. 'And I'm not, am I?'

He laughed. 'There's nothing depraved about a man wanting the woman he's married to.'

'There is when that's all there is to it. Technically you're no better than any other man who forces a woman to ... to subjugate herself to his demands!'

'The word you're looking for is rape,' he countered smoothly. 'And I haven't forced you into anything—not yet. Neither am I expecting to find it necessary. It's a poor man who can't manage to rouse a woman.'

Kim's hands were clenched tightly in her lap, her pulses racing madly. 'Even when the woman happens to regard the man with loathing?'

'Even more so then. Hate is a positive emotion, green eyes. It can make for just as exciting a relationship as its counterpart.'

'How would *you* know?'

'Oh, I once fell in love.' His tone was sardonic. 'It put me at a distinct disadvantage and taught me a lesson I've never forgotten. There's only one place for a woman in a man's life, and that's in his bed.'

It was too dark to see his features clearly, but his posture, though unchanged, had stiffened. Kim said softly, 'She must have let you down very badly.'

'She did me a favour. For that I can even feel grateful. Nothing lasts, so make the most of it while you've got it.'

'Including me, I suppose.'

'Including you.'

Without altering her tone, Kim said, 'But with me you made one small mistake. You put our relationship on a different footing from the rest. Suppose I decide to make the best of things too? Supposing I refuse to go along with your plans for when we get back to England? You'd be stuck with a wife then—*and* I'd be able to claim maintenance from you.'

The pause was lengthy. 'Are you threatening me?' he asked at last in deceptively quiet tones.

'No.' The palms of her hands were sweating, but she refused to back down now. 'Just pointing out that the advantages aren't all on your side. Out here I'm helpless, I admit that. I got myself into this mess and I have to buy myself out of it. Only don't expect me to simply fade out of your life when you say without some form of compensation.'

He was very still. 'And what price do you put on your . . . favours?'

So what if the whole affair *had* gone further than she had intended? Kim asked herself defensively. Nothing on earth would keep her tied to Dave once she had the chance to be free of him, but there was no reason to let him think it was going to be that easy. 'A very high one,' she said.

'Right.' He got to his feet and moved towards her, the light from the storm lamp revealing the mocking twist to his lips. Thunder grumbled again as he bent to scoop her bodily from the chair, echoing the pounding of her heartbeats. 'So let's see if you're going to be worth it.'

Kim didn't open her eyes when Dave got up from the other bed at first light. Not for the life of her could she have faced up to that derisory smile of his at such an hour. She lay there motionless, face down in the pillows, listening to him moving about the room.

Only when the door finally closed behind him did she roll slowly over to gaze blindly at the flaking ceiling, her mind roving back relentlessly over the past hours. There had been no element of tenderness in any moment of the time she had spent in Dave's arms, no gentleness in his passionate possession of her. Yet she could not shut her mind to the knowledge of her own dawning response, the awakening of a need she had had to fight to overcome. Shame stirred within her. She was no better than he was—worse, in fact, because he didn't pretend to be any better than he was. The emotions he had aroused in her last night had nothing at all to do with love. That was a point on which it was impossible to deceive herself. Dave

Nelson wasn't a man she could ever love. Especially not now.

She got up at seven, unable to bear the torture of inactivity any longer. Her eyes, reflected in the mirror over the chest of drawers, looked bruised. She ran a dispassionate glance over her slender reflection, came back to her mouth and firmed her jaw. No use in dwelling on it. It had happened, and nothing could alter that fact. She supposed she should be grateful that he had seen fit to actually grace her with his name first. Knowing what she knew now, she doubted that anyone would have raised a hand to help her even if he had abducted her here by force. These men lived by their own set of rules. It just went to prove that removed from the restraining influence of the greater community for any length of time man would always revert to the savage. Dave was simply the leader of a tribe, the bull ape with the greatest strength. It wouldn't, she thought with satire, have seemed at all out of place had he stood over her and voiced his triumph in a spate of chest-beating last night.

And what had happened last night would certainly happen again, unless she did get away from here. The problem was, which was the worst of two evils—Dave, or the very real possibility of being stuck down in Freetown without help of any kind? Supposing Chris refused point blank to loan her money. What then? She had no way of forcing him to do anything he didn't want to do, and he was by no means the man she had once known. Put like that it was perhaps better to stay and face the devil one knew. At least this way she was assured of getting back to England and home—eventually.

There seemed little point in leaving her suitcase packed any longer. The wardrobe had plenty of room left in it for her things, despite the couple of lightweight suits and several pairs of slacks and shirts already hanging there. Kim wondered why any man should need this amount of clothing on a mine site, until she realised that there would more than likely be weekends down in town as well as the annual local leave allowed by the Company. Chris had rarely mentioned how he spent his leisure time, she recalled. His letters had been taken up with the work, the climate and, initially anyway, how much he missed her.

Which gave rise to another thought. What would happen about such weekends now that Dave had a wife round his neck? Would he forgo them for the rest of his time here, or would he condescend to take her with him? One thing seemed certain, he would not be leaving her here alone for any length of time. He had made it quite clear that he trusted neither her nor his fellow men very far, and Dave wasn't the type to risk being done down by anyone.

She kept out a blue cotton wrap, belting it securely about her waist before going out to the bathroom. This morning the water was just warm enough to be pleasant. Evidently Patrick had heard her moving around and accurately assessed her priorities. She could hear him whistling in the kitchen, and reminded herself that this morning that particular part of her temporary home was due for a turn-out. No doubt Patrick would be more than a little resentful of interference on her part, but she couldn't ignore the condition of those cupboards for five more weeks.

She tackled him on the subject immediately after breakfast, to be blithely informed that the ants kept the other insects out of the stores.

'So does hot water and repellant powder,' she replied firmly. 'You can see to the cupboards while I scour out the containers. That way the whole job should be finished by lunchtime.'

Patrick looked doubtful. 'The boss not like it, missis,' he muttered.

'The boss won't know about it, unless you tell him.' That was almost an invitation to conspire against Dave's authority, she realised, but it was too late now to rephrase. 'It shouldn't take long,' she repeated hastily.

The stock of tinned goods seemed all right after a wipe over with a damp cloth, although there were a couple of dented cans of meat which Kim ordered thrown away for safety's sake. When it came to dried goods kept in containers it was another matter. There were weevils in the biscuits, and a kind of green mould growing up the sides of the flour bin. Kim thought of the sauce Patrick had served over the fruit pudding the night before and wondered at her own constitution. No wonder it had tasted so odd! At any rate, the rest of the flour was fit only for the compost heap—or whatever the equivalent was in this part of the world.

In the end she dumped practically all the dry stores in the kitchen into a paper sack Patrick found for her, and put them outside the door for disposal. With the containers clean and dry she would feel better, she decided, if the contents were fresh too. Patrick informed her that new supplies must be fetched from the depot behind the clubhouse, and that the order must be signed by Dave himself. Kim made out a list in readiness against his return, whenever that might be, and left it on the dining table while she returned to the kitchen to inspect Pat's handiwork, only to find that he was still only halfway through his allotted task. Making an African move at anything faster than a snail's pace was nigh on impossible, apparently. One either got into the same rhythm of things or did the work oneself. In this case, Kim plumped for the latter course, and despatched him to clean the living rooms while she got on with it.

As perspiration was liable to break out at even the slightest exertion during daylight hours, she was already wet through before she began the new job, and the steam rising from the bucket of hot water did nothing to help. Despite the band fastening back her hair it kept falling over her face, making her hotter still. She pushed at it irritably, leaving a streak of dirt down one cheek, then sat back on her heels to try fastening it up out of the way altogether. When she turned her head Dave was standing in the doorway, face tersely set.

'What in hell's name do you think you're doing?' he demanded.

Kim stared back at him warily, not liking his expression, his tone, or anything about his appearance in general. 'Something that should have been done a long time ago,' she answered at last. 'I don't think this place has had a thorough clean-out since it was built!'

'Then you should have set Pat to it.' He sounded furious. 'What do you think he gets paid for?' He took the two steps which brought him across to her, and yanked her roughly to her feet, his fingers plucking at the shoulder seam of her shirt and drawing it out from the skin. 'You're soaked, you little idiot. Haven't you got more sense!'

'Apparently not.' Kim made herself stand still in his grasp. 'And isn't it a bit late to be getting concerned about my welfare?'

'I'm concerned with everyone's welfare here—including yours! You're not even used to the damned climate yet, and I find you ...' He stopped, clamped his teeth together, said through them, 'Don't you attempt to do this again, do you hear? You're no servant!'

What was in a name? she thought with cynicism. 'I needed something to pass the time with,' she said as he released her. 'Assuming the other job doesn't start till after the weekend.'

'That's right, it doesn't. Monday morning you'll have all the work you want. Till then you'll just have to get by.'

'Shall I be working in the office?'

'No, here at the house. I don't want you round the site unless I'm with you.' He moved impatiently. 'Go and get changed. We're having lunch at the club. And don't say you're not hungry this time.'

'I wasn't going to,' she rejoined without expression, and walked out of the room.

Looking distinctly accusing. Patrick was despatched to prepare another cool shower, while she went to the bedroom to find fresh clothing. The soiled garments she had put into the laundry bin behind the door only that morning had already gone. Kim slung in the cotton pants and shirt she had just taken off and got out a dress to wear for lunch, then shrugged into the blue robe for her trip to the bathroom. Patrick had not forgotten to provide a clean towel. It was hanging on the nail provided for it just outside the cubicle. Kim went in and hooked shut the bamboo door, then slid out of the wrap and pushed it through the narrow gap between wall and roof to hang it beside the towel. She was tucking her hair up under her shower cap when Dave sauntered out from the kitchen on to the veranda, stopping a few feet away to lean an arm along the rail and survey the tangle of undergrowth spreading across the gap between house and jungle.

'We could do with a flame-thrower to keep that lot back,' he remarked conversationally. 'Chopping it back is virtually useless in this climate, especially at this time of the year.' He glanced her way when she made no answer, a glint of amusement in the eyes which slid over her capped head and the tops of her bare shoulders. 'Get a move on. I told Luke we'd see him in half an hour.'

He was doing this purposely, she thought, intending to disconcert her. Well, she wouldn't give him that satisfaction. She finished tucking in her hair, then put up a hand and pulled the rope which tipped water over her, trying not to gasp as it streamed over her face. When she was through she reached outside and drew in the towel, wrapping it around her and towelling herself slowly so that perspiration wouldn't break out anew. She was about to remove the towel and exchange it for her wrap when a movement down near her foot caught her eye. Kim felt the quick beading of her upper lip as she gazed in motionless horror at the scorpion clinging to the corner of the material where it touched the floor. Where it had come from she had no idea. Right at the moment it hardly seemed to matter. The question was what did she do now?

Her voice when it came was low and tremulous. 'Dave, there's a scorpion in here.'

'Well, don't argue with it,' he advised without concern. 'Come on out.'

'I can't. It's . . . it's on my towel.'

He came alert. 'Where?'

'Down near the floor. It isn't moving, just sitting there.'

Dave came up quickly. 'Reach out an arm and unhook the door. Do it slowly. They can shift like lightning.'

Kim obeyed without hesitation, her fingers finding the catch by instinct as she dared not take her eyes off the insect so close to her bare foot. Dave pulled the door open slowly, taking care to block any sudden stream of light. One look at the scorpion and he sprang into action, sending it spinning with a kick which missed Kim's toes by a bare fraction of an inch and drawing her out into the open. She clung to him unashamedly, everything forgotten for the moment but her narrow escape from a particularly horrible death. Only the feel of rough denim against her skin finally brought her back to the realisation of what she was doing. Face flaming red, she clutched the slipping towel about her and pushed herself away from the man whose arms had so readily held her, seeing the smile flicker at his lips.

'Your life and your modesty, both saved,' he said

with satire. 'Don't worry, I'm not about to take advantage of your gratitude. You'd better get some clothes on while I get rid of our friend in there.'

Kim fled to the bedroom, resisting the urge to wedge a chair beneath the door handle with an effort. She was trembling again, only this time it was in sheer disgust at her own weakness. She hated Dave Nelson with everything that was in her, yet a moment ago she had flung herself into his arms in search of security, clung to him as if she wanted him never to let her go. And all because of an incident she could have handled herself if she hadn't panicked. There had been no real danger, of course. She had been protected by the towel. Dave would have seen that instantly, but the excuse to make a fool of her had been too good to miss.

Lunch at the club was still an ordeal, but she got through it. She wondered how long it was going to take for her presence to be accepted as normal by the men working for the mining company, for conversation to retain its flow when she entered a room. It wasn't even as if they were so woman-starved, she reflected over coffee. There was a whole township over the ridge.

Luke spent the greater part of the meal discussing new safety measures against the effects of the coming rains. Last night's threatened storm had not reached them, but today the sky was heavily hazed and there were black clouds on the forested green hills beyond the mine. What it would be like when the rains really got into their stride, Kim hated to think. Soggy oppressiveness, the smell of rotting vegetation, mud everywhere. She would need some boots and a raincoat unless she wanted to spend most of her time confined to the house.

With a small sense of shock, Kim realised just how far her acceptance of her position must have gone when she could plan ahead like this. In just a few days Dave had managed to subdue her fighting spirit to an extent where she was beginning to sit back and acknowledge his right to keep her here. She would get even with him for all he was doing to her, she vowed fiercely. Some time, somehow, she would make him pay full measure for every minute of these weeks he was forcing her to spend with him!

One of the waiters came across to tell Dave he was wanted on the site telephone. Left alone with Luke, Kim said into the pause, 'Do you think you could teach me to play billiards some time?'

Surprise gave way to a grin. 'Snooker,' he corrected. 'There's a difference. I'd be glad to, providing...'

'Providing it meets with Dave's approval,' she finished for him evenly. 'Any reason why it shouldn't?'

His shrug was easy. 'He might not like the idea of you coming to the club without him. Can't say I'd be all that keen on having you run round loose myself. Remember what happened that first night?'

'That was before I became the exclusive property of one man,' she retorted softly. 'Nobody is going to start a fight over Dave Nelson's woman, not if they want to keep their job. I know it, you know it and they know it. So where's the problem?'

Luke jerked a thumb over his shoulder. 'There's the problem. And I'm not criticising him for it either. If I'd got a wife who looked like you do in a

91

place like this I wouldn't trust her alone with my closest friend!'

'You don't appear to have a very high opinion of my code of ethics,' she said.

He looked at her uncertainly for a moment, then his forehead cleared. 'Sorry,' he offered on a sheepish note. 'I meant I wouldn't trust the friend.'

'Have you known Dave long?' she asked obliquely.

'We met in Dakar some years back. He was working out at Zouerate in Mauritania at the time, and I was drifting between jobs. I went back to England for a spell, couldn't settle and took out a contract with this outfit. Dave was already here when I arrived a couple of years ago.'

Kim said slowly, 'You think rather a lot of him, don't you, Luke?'

It was a moment before he answered that one. 'Let's say he's one man I know I could rely on in a tight spot. There was one time...' He paused, shook his head, took out cigarettes. 'Forget it. He wouldn't appreciate me telling you the tale.'

Kim didn't press him for the rest of the story. Something inside her didn't want to hear it. Luke had one view of the man she had married, herself another, and that was how it was going to stay. Nothing must be allowed to cloud the issue. She allowed her eyes to move beyond Luke's shoulder to the open door of the room and the view into the corridor where Dave stood talking into the wall telephone. He had one foot raised to the lower rung of the chair set beneath the handset and was leaning forward with his arm resting along his bent knee. Seen in profile his features looked hewn from solid rock by a sculptor more interested in plane and angle than aesthetic appeal. Not a handsome face, but certainly one to attract attention. He looked what he was, she reflected. An iron man, tough, unyielding and virtually indestructible. No doubt some women found that combination exciting, even irresistible, but she wasn't one of them. All she wanted was some way of getting under that unfeeling hide of his, some way of hurting him so badly that he would carry the scars for the rest of his life.

It was then that the idea took root. Once, a long time ago, a woman had managed to hurt him, much as he tried to smother the memory in cynicism. Supposing, just supposing she could make him fall for her, wouldn't that provide her with the sharpest weapon of all? And why not? True, he was probably a tougher proposition than he would have been then, but she already had a head start in the field of attraction, as one might say, and certainly nothing to lose. And what a revenge that would be! Almost worth the degradation he was forcing on her.

She realised suddenly that Dave had replaced the receiver and was gazing straight back across the room at her, brows raised quizzically. Kim lowered her eyes swiftly, wondering what she had revealed of her thoughts in that moment's unawareness. Any campaign such as the one she had just been contemplating presented a very real challenge, she acknowledged. He was too astute to be taken in by half-hearted tactics. She wasn't at all sure that she was equal to projecting herself physically into a role against which all her sensibilities would be

93

crying out.

'I'm going into town,' he announced when he reached the table. 'Want to come along for the ride?'

Kim looked up at him quickly, not certain whether the question was meant for her or Luke. His expression was enigmatic, giving away nothing of what was going on behind the steady grey eyes. 'It would make a change,' she conceded after a brief moment.

Luke accompanied them as far as the main door, casting a knowledgeable glance at the sky. 'Going to get some rain before long,' he stated. 'That road was a river the other night. Think you'll make it back in time?'

'If we don't we'll swim for it,' was the unperturbed reply. 'Might be a good idea to get a team up there to cut a couple of drain channels before the first big storm. I've a feeling we're going to get them early this year.'

In the car Kim said diffidently, 'What happens on the site when the rains really get into their stride? Surely you can't carry on working during the storms?'

'Depends on the severity. If we stood the men down every time it rained we might as well close down altogether during the wet. It's a hell of a time, but we get through.'

'Only this year you'll not be seeing much of it.'

'No.'

She waited a moment before voicing the next question. 'Are you planning to come back?'

'Certainly not to Pillai. Three years in one place is enough. Luke takes over when I go. He'll probably do another spell, unless something crops up to change his mind.'

'Like what, for instance?'

He gave her a brief glance. 'How would I know? He's got a year of this present contract to run yet. After that anything might happen. In this line you take it as it comes.' He changed gear, added casually, 'It's as well that we will be leaving in a few weeks. You'd never stand a whole season up here.'

What he probably meant, she thought, was that he himself would be bored to death with her in that length of time. And this was the man she was hoping to bring to his knees in five short weeks! With grim determination she brushed aside the defeatism threatening to swamp her. She had his interest now, didn't she? And she hadn't even begun her campaign to increase it. The fact that she wasn't at all sure how she was going to begin it she also pushed to the back of her mind. Where an affair of this nature was concerned instinct must play a large part.

It took them twenty minutes driving to reach the town by way of the tortuously twisting track. Dave told her that the men cut through the forest to reach the site each shift, but the paths they made were not wide enough to take a car. The town itself was larger than Kim had anticipated, a haphazard grouping of stained stucco and corrugated iron laced through with mud streets, and overhung with palm and trees like cedars. The house outside which Dave eventually stopped the car was one of the better kept ones, its tin roof free of the rust which was attacking its neighbours.

'This won't take long,' he said, and disappeared

indoors, leaving Kim to face the frank stares of the populace. It was stifling in the car, the humidity hanging like a pall. Kim eased her back away from the seat and felt her shirt clinging to her. She got out of the car and leaned against a wing instead, finding some small relief in the open air. The cloud had built up from the north until it covered the whole sky, thick and dark and threatening. Thunder was rolling in the hills again, nearer this time, with the occasional flash of lightning thrown in for good measure. She wished Dave would hurry up. Being caught out in a storm like the one she was certain was coming would be no joke.

Two boys approached near to the car. They looked like brothers, one perhaps ten years of age, the other twelve. They stood gazing at her with solemn curiosity, the younger one wearing a miner's white helmet which rested on the tops of his ears and wobbled dangerously every time he moved his head.

'Cigarettes?' asked the elder one hopefully, encouraged by Kim's involuntary smile. 'You give cigarettes, missis?'

'Sorry, I haven't got any.' Kim spread her hands to show their emptiness, wishing she had something more suitable to offer the pair in compensation.

Dave came out of the house, accompanied to the door by two giggling young women wearing European dress. 'Hop it, you two,' he said briefly but not unkindly to the boys, and tossed the older one a coin before getting in the car.

'What were they after?' he asked Kim when they were moving again. She told him and he grinned.

'Got a real taste for tobacco, those two. Stunt their growth if they're not careful.'

'You seem to know them,' she murmured.

'They belong to my foreman—the man I've just been to see. He had a leg broken the other night, and was worried about his family. The Company takes care of cases like his, only they never will believe it without being reassured a dozen times or more. What did you think of his wives?'

Kim glanced at him quickly. '*Both* of them?'

'Why not? He's a Muslim; they're allowed four.' He was heading back the way they had come. 'I'll drop you off at the house and get back to the site before this lot breaks.'

His timing was out. They were only halfway back when a particularly loud clap of thunder heralded the sudden smashing roar of the torrent. Kim had never seen rain like this, a solid wall of water which turned the track into a quagmire within seconds and made driving an impossibility. Dave drew up at the side of the track and switched off the engine. 'We'll have to sit it out till it eases up,' he said. 'We're liable to run off firm ground and get bogged down.'

'You call this firm?' she asked, trying not to sound too perturbed. 'It's running like a river out there!'

'So long as it is running we're okay. It's when it backs up that the trouble comes.' He reached for cigarettes, caught her expression as the thunder crashed again, added easily, 'It sounds worse than it is. Everything's larger than life in these parts. Smoke?'

She took one, glad to have something other than

97

the storm on which to concentrate. Dave lit hers first and then his own, shook out the match and tossed it out through the opened window. For a moment or two there was a silence punctuated only by the unremitting downpour.

'How do you stand six months of this?' Kim burst out at last, unable to bear just sitting there listening any longer.

'The first year is the worst,' he returned. 'After that you get to accept anything the climate throws at you. Some of the men arrange to take their annual leave during the rains and head for the north.'

'But not you,' she hazarded.

He lifted his shoulders. 'One place is as good as another on leave. I've spent mine mostly down in Freetown.'

'I suppose you go there quite often.'

'At the weekends.' He added lightly, 'Behave yourself and I might even take you. You didn't get much chance to see the place on either of your other two visits.'

'No.' Kim forced herself to adopt the same lightness of tone. 'I must say, I'd hate to have to go back home and admit that the only part of Sierra Leone I'd really seen was a mining camp in the mountains.'

'What about your friends in London?' he asked unexpectedly. 'Have you let them know your plans?'

'*Your* plans, you mean,' she couldn't resist saying pointedly.

'It amounts to the same thing. Have you?'

'I only have one close friend—the girl I shared a flat with.'

'Shared?'

'Naturally I had to tell her to find someone else when I came out to Africa. I couldn't have afforded to pay my share of the rent while I was away. In any case, I wasn't sure how long I was going to be away.'

Dave's expression was curious. 'Do you ever stop to think anything through before you act?'

'Not very often,' she admitted ruefully, and then on a harder note, 'Though I've a feeling I might in future.'

'Come on.' He was smiling again. 'It isn't that bad. I got the distinct impression you might be starting to enjoy our arrangement.'

Kim felt her face go hot. 'There's a vast difference between enjoyment and sufferance,' she flashed. 'If there's one thing I have learned about you it's that you're totally devoid of any kind of humanity, so obviously it's a waste of time to put up any resistance. Our arrangement, as you call it, is something I have to tolerate in order to get back home. I don't like it, but there's very little—short of murder—that I can do about it.'

There was a glint in the grey eyes as he studied her. 'You're a liar,' he said in almost conversational tones. 'Basically you want me as much as I want you, only it goes against your juvenile code of ethics to admit it. There's no woman so green as to really believe the kind of rubbish you threw at me the other night. All you were trying to do is provide yourself with a defence against your own inclinations.'

'That's not true!' She said it through clenched teeth. 'You might consider yourself irresistible to

99

all women, but I can tell you that so far as I'm concerned you're just a means to an end. If you want to know, it makes me shudder to be touched by you!'

'So I'd noticed.' There was irony in his tone. 'All right, stick to your own version. You don't like anything about our relationship, least of all me.' He reached out and took the scarcely smoked cigarette from her, tossed it along with his own through the window into the rain and drew her towards him, smiling mockingly at her involuntary resistance. 'Go ahead and fight. I like a touch of spirit in my women!'

Kim closed her eyes as his head bent towards her, steeling herself for the touch of his lips on hers. When nothing happened she opened them again quickly, to find his eyes only inches away from hers with amusement in their depths. His hand moved to cover her heart and register the increasing beat, moved again to slide to the base of her throat and caress the line of her collarbone with unbelievable sensitivity, stretching every nerve in her body to tingling awareness. She quivered as his lips found the corner of her mouth, fighting for control over her own treacherous emotions, hating herself almost as much as him for not having the strength of will to combat the sheer sensation of his knowledgeable touch. Three days, she thought wildly, and already he had reduced her to this stage of debasement. What kind of a person was she that a lifetime's principles could rest on such shaky foundations?

But such a response was necessary to her plans for his downfall, another part of her mind recalled.

How could she hope to achieve the kind of revenge she hoped for unless she used every weapon at her command? To reach the man inside she first had to satisfy the cruder emotions. That was an inescapable fact. It was for that reason and that reason alone that she finally allowed herself to relax the frigid tension of her body a little and be drawn further into his arms, to part her lips to his demanding kiss and give some measure of return. The end justified the means, she told herself emphatically. The end always justified the means!

Nevertheless, she couldn't quite meet his eyes when he finally let her go. There might have been justification in the relative abandon of these last few minutes, but now that they were over little pride in herself or her motives. That had been no response at the cost of inclination. If she were honest with herself she had to admit that she had wanted to respond. Dave had not been overestimating his power over her when he had declared himself capable of arousing her any time he wanted to. He knew her better than she knew herself.

'Better than I hoped for,' he said softly.

'Better than you deserve,' she flashed back, rallying her flagging spirit by sheer effort of will. Her head lifted, chin jutting. 'All right, so you proved your point. You must be feeling very proud of yourself.'

'Not unduly. Wondering might be a better word.' There was an odd note in his voice. 'You've got the strength of mind to keep yourself well in check, yet you purposely gave way to me just then. Why?'

She said in low tones, 'You know why.'

'Because you couldn't help yourself?' He studied her, lips twisting slightly. 'I don't think so. I think you had other motives.'

'Such as?' Despite everything she could do to keep it steady her voice had a tremor in it.

'Such as the hope that by making yourself—pleasant, shall we say—to me you might find a chink somewhere that you could get at me through. You're not all that good at concealing your thoughts, sweetheart. I knew you were plotting something when I caught you giving me that calculating look while I was on the phone a while back. Well, keep on trying, by all means. With a little more practice you might even learn to really let yourself go!'

Kim gazed at him in defeat, aware now that he had been playing with her as a cat might play with a mouse. It was hopeless asking, but she made one more attempt to reach his better instincts. 'Dave,' she said shakily, 'let me leave. I don't mean anything to you.'

'Wrong again. You mean a whole lot.' His thumb caressed the point of her chin with deliberation. 'You're a very desirable woman, and you happen to be my wife. While those two circumstances continue to apply you're staying right here with me.' He reached forward and switched on the ignition. 'The rain's letting up a bit. We should make it to the house now.'

They made it silence on Kim's part. The clearing had several muddy rivers running through it where the car tracks had ridged up the earth. Dave brought the car to a halt as close to the steps as possible and was out and round before Kim could move, lifting her across the stretch of mud on to the veranda. The rain might have lessened in force, but even so the shoulders of his shirt were soaked through. He dropped her to the floor and went on into the house ahead of her.

She was mixing herself a drink when he came back from the bedroom buttoning a dry shirt.

'Isn't it a bit early for that?' he said.

'Is it?' She turned with the glass in her hand, her eyes unnaturally bright. 'Perhaps I feel in need of it. It's hardly to be wondered at.'

He came over purposefully and took the glass from her. 'You'll come through without this. I have enough problems with you without adding alcohol to them.'

'Problems? With me?' She gave a short laugh. 'You should make up your mind, Dave. A little while ago you seemed convinced that you had me completely under control.'

There was a pause and a slight change of expression before he said brusquely, 'We're not talking about the same things. Are you going to keep off this stuff till evening, or do I lock it up?'

She lifted her hands in a weary little gesture of acceptance. 'I'll leave it alone. Do you want me to pour that back?'

'No, seeing that it's already out I'll drink it myself.' The jeering smile was back. 'I'm used to it and you're not. That's the difference.'

'It's not the only one,' she retorted, but her voice lacked force. 'Are you going out again?'

'Yes. Happy?'

'Ecstatic.' She walked past him without another

word, crossing into the bedroom and closing the door.

The car left five minutes later. Face down on the bed, Kim examined the weave of the spread immediately below her eyes and calculated that she had roughly thirty-five more days of this to get through before England and home became more than a dream. Thirty-five more days, and an equal number of nights. And when she did get back to London, what then? She had no job, nowhere to live and less than a hundred pounds in the world. But she would starve rather than accept money from Dave. That would be the final degradation.

CHAPTER FIVE

THERE was another storm during the weekend, followed by three days when the whole site was blanketed in thick dark cloud which trapped the moist heat beneath it in devitalising oppressiveness. Despite the sheer effort of any kind of movement, the mine continued to function to its normal work load, only pausing for a total of three hours over the whole period. The men groused as a matter of course about the 'Goddamned climate', but not one of them seemed unduly affected by the seasonal changes.

Kim had begun work on the pay sheets on the Monday, working for three hours in the morning and another three in the late afternoon. With the help of a rather antiquated adding machine Dave had brought down from the office for her she found the job less difficult than she had imagined. She was finished with the actual pay chits by Wednesday lunchtime, the piles of envelopes ready labelled and stacked into trays in preparation for their despatch to the wages office where the clerks would fill them. She stretched and pushed back her chair from the desk in the corner of the living room where she had been working. Tomorrow would be soon enough to start entering up her figures in the books, which gave her this afternoon free of any kind of effort if she wished it.

The torpor outside was almost matched by the closeness of the atmosphere indoors. Where Dave himself was at this time she had no idea. Nor, she told herself, did she particularly care. For the last couple of days he had stayed away from the house until late afternoon, returning in time for sun-downers and snacks, and an hour or so's rest until dinner. Their life together had already taken on a pattern, she reflected now. One she accepted because there was no other choice, but one against which her spirit still rebelled. To Dave she was simply an amenity, a companion to while away the hours between one day's work and the next. Not for anything would Kim have consciously admitted that the daylight hours when he wasn't with her seemed to stretch to infinity because of it, nor that the awakening of vitality in her coincided as much with the sound of his returning car as the onset of the slightly cooler evenings.

Patrick served the light lunch of salad and cold meat which she had asked for, and asked if she would want tea as usual at four-thirty. On impulse, Kim told him to take the rest of the day off. To-night they would eat at the club, and if Dave didn't like it that was just too bad. It was more than time she had a change herself.

She spent the afternoon lazily with a detective novel chosen from the rack of paperbacks in the living room, trying her best to ignore the stifling humidity. There was thunder rumbling in the distance again, and the stillness which presaged an-other storm. In a week or two the violence of the elements would be on the wane, but the rain would continue to fall with increasing regularity right through July and August before beginning to taper off slowly towards the dryer season. For Kim the country had absolutely nothing to recommend it. A hot, wet hell of a place she couldn't wait to leave.

It was only when she decided to take a shower and change her dress that she remembered about the water. Patrick kept a large saucepan constantly heating on the wood-fired stove, topping up the shower tank as required to produce a luke-warm spray. His departure after Kim's unexpected gift of a free half day must have been a hasty one, for when she went through to the kitchen she found the stove cold and the saucepan almost empty. Filling the latter at the pump presented no particular problem, heating it up was another matter. Kim had seen Patrick light the stove on occasion, but had only a vague idea of how to go about it herself. There was a pile of ready cut wood stacked in a bin in one corner of the kitchen, and some old magazines stuffed behind it which she assumed were intended for getting the blaze started. She made a small heap of crumpled pages and wood in the stove, and put a match to them hopefully. The paper smouldered blackly at the edge and went out again. She lit another match and applied that, this time holding it to the paper until it almost burned down to her fingers. The whole page caught and flared with unexpected rapidity, and Kim snatched back her hand as flame seared briefly across it, ignoring the pain for the moment as she defeatedly watched the blaze die out without having done more than singe the ends of a couple of sticks.

It was only when she turned her palm over that

she realised the extent of the reddened area, and by that time it was really beginning to hurt. She found something to wrap round it to exclude the air from the surface, and tried to recall what is was that one put on burns. Bicarb, she believed, in the absence of anything better, only she couldn't remember having seen any when she had cleared out the cupboards.

There would be a first-aid box somewhere around, she realised. She went through to the living room to look for it, cradling the injured palm in her other hand. She hadn't heard the car, and was startled when Dave appeared in the doorway, accompanied by another roll of thunder.

'Going to be another big one,' he observed unnecessarily, then his eyes dropped to her hand wrapped in the clean handkerchief and his tone altered. 'What have you done?'

Kim told him. 'It's nothing serious,' she finished, trying not to show that it was giving her any pain. 'I was looking for the first-aid box.'

He came over and took the hand in his, unwinding the handkerchief and gently straightening out her palm to look at the burn. 'This needs attention,' he pronounced. 'I'd better take you up to the treatment room and let Doc Selby take a look at it.'

'Oh, I'm sure that isn't necessary,' Kim protested. 'Really, Dave...'

'I'll decide what's necessary. It's too easy to get an infection in this climate. Just as a matter of interest, why were you trying to light the stove in the first place?'

'I gave Patrick the afternoon off. I thought we

might have dinner at the club.' She met his gaze defiantly. 'Any objections?'

His grin was sudden and unexpected. 'None that I can think of offhand. You don't have to sound so belligerent about it. I'm willing to agree that you're due to an occasional outing, even in this benighted place.' He slid his hand under her elbow and turned her towards the door. 'But first some treatment for that hand.'

They were in the car and moving up the gradient towards the club when he said casually, 'How do you feel about spending the weekend down in town?'

Kim glanced at him quickly. 'With you?'

'Who else?'

She was silent for a long moment before saying softly, 'Aren't you afraid I might try running off again?'

'No.' He swung the wheel. 'You've nowhere to run—unless you were thinking about Adams again.'

'What would be the use?'

'Exactly. I'm glad you're beginning to see sense regarding that character at last.' There was a brief pause, then he added, 'Still feel like running away from me, do you?'

A couple of days ago Kim wouldn't have had to think twice about the answer to that one. Now, she found herself hesitating before saying slowly, 'Like you just said, I've nowhere to go. You don't have to worry about that, Dave. I'll stick to the so-called bargain we made.'

His mouth hardened a little. 'You know, I'm beginning to get just a bit tired of this attitude of yours. You came into this with your eyes wide open, so stop trying to make me out to be the villain of the piece. Sure, I wanted you, and maybe I did manipulate matters so that I could have you, but I did it legally and without any false promises.'

She swallowed tightly. 'Not even a marriage licence necessarily gives a man total rights over a woman—certainly not in England.'

'But this isn't England, as I keep having to remind you, and I'm not interested in the small print. You came up here looking for a man, and you found one. I don't think I'm flattering myself too much in judging myself a better catch than Adams—even on a temporary basis.' There was irony in his tone. 'You might tell yourself that you want these next few weeks over as quickly as possible, but I'll guarantee that you'll never forget them!'

'Modesty isn't exactly one of your strong points, is it?' she came back with sarcasm in an attempt to conceal her reactions to that statement. 'Self-praise is no particular recommendation.'

His smile was grimly amused. 'Neither is naïveté. Do you think I don't know the difference between genuine non-response and determined control?'

Kim looked out of the window, conscious of his closeness and the certainty of those hard brown hands on the wheel. He knew too much about everything—especially women. Who was it who had said that familiarity breeds contempt?

The mine's resident doctor was a taciturn man in his fifties whom Kim had spoken with only once before. He gave the burned palm a somewhat cursory examination, slapped on a thick yellow paste which smelled horrible and bound up the hand with a crêpe bandage.

'Shouldn't have any trouble with it providing you keep it dry,' he muttered. 'Take that off in the morning and let the air get to it.'

However obnoxious the remedy it certainly took the pain away, Kim reflected on the way back to the house. All the same, it seemed a lot of fuss over what was after all only a very minor injury. As it was, it was going to be quite a problem washing with one hand wrapped up like this.

The threatened storm broke just after they got indoors, the rain sweeping in from the forest with a suddenness that startled despite the anticipation. Dave lit the stove, and suggested drinks while they waited for the water to heat, standing in the doorway, glass in hand, to view the rain with appreciative if unthrilled eyes.

'At least it cools things down a bit,' he remarked.

Kim said, 'I didn't think the climate bothered you one way or the other.'

'I don't think it does any good to swear about it,' with a shrug, 'but I wouldn't call it the best on earth either. The only real thing to be said in its favour is that we're better off than those poor devils in Mali dying from drought.' He drained the glass and turned back into the room to put it down. The trays of wage envelopes were still on the desk where Kim had left them earlier. He went over to flip through the stack of time sheets. 'How long before you finish these?'

'They are finished,' she told him. 'Since lunchtime.' She couldn't help adding with a hint of malice, 'I'd have done something about getting them up to the wages office if I'd had any transport available—plus, of course, your permission to leave the house.'

Dave straightened, looking across at her with a faint smile. 'You spoiling for a fight?'

'I don't want to fight with anyone,' she came back promptly. 'All I am trying to say is that I'd appreciate some means of getting away from the house occasionally during the day. I know you said you didn't want me running around the site, but I'd steer clear of any trouble.'

'I didn't know you could drive,' he commented after a moment.

'Chris taught me before he came out to Africa.' She kept her tone emotionless. 'I've never driven a Land-Rover before, but I've watched you with the gears and I think I could handle it. It isn't as though I would take it off the mine. I'd not get past the gate.'

'No,' he agreed dryly, 'you wouldn't.' He studied her thoughtfully. 'What about the hand?'

'That will be better in a day or so. It's only a superficial burn.' She was trying not to plead with him. 'It isn't so much to ask.'

'All right,' he said. 'When we get back from Freetown we'll see what we can do. There's a spare car you could use.' A glint of mockery in his eyes, he registered her expression. 'Battle won too easily for you?'

Kim had to smile. 'I was expecting rather more opposition,' she admitted. 'You're not usually so ready to be helpful.'

'You haven't tried asking me for anything before.' His tone changed abruptly. 'That water should be hot by now. Do you want first go in the shower?'

She shook her head. 'I'll have to make do with a wash tonight. I'd only get this dressing wet. I'd be grateful if you'd pour me some water into a bowl and leave it in the kitchen. I can manage in there.'

His smile was sudden and satirical. 'If you need any help just give me a shout.'

'I'll cope, thanks.'

'If it kills you.' He put the empty glass down on the table as he went from the room.

Kim did cope, though with some difficulty. Dressed again, she made her way back to the bedroom to finish off her toilet, confident that Dave would have finished dressing by now. She stopped nonplussed in the doorway when she found him lounging on his bed with a cigarette smouldering between his fingers while he went through a sheaf of papers. He had changed his working denims for slacks, but had not yet donned a shirt. He looked up at her entry, lifting a inquiring eyebrow when she failed to move further into the room.

'Something bothering you?'

'I—I thought you would be ready,' she got out.

'So I am—almost. Where's the rush?'

'There isn't one. It's just that—' she hesitated—'I want to brush my hair and put on some lipstick.'

Amusement came into his face. 'Is there a taboo against a man watching his wife paint the lily?'

'I don't imagine so.' Kim wasn't at all sure why she should feel so adamantly against having him there while she performed the finishing touches necessary to all women before they went anywhere, and the realisation that she was being irrational irritated her beyond measure. 'I have a right to expect *some* privacy, even from you,' she added stubbornly.

The amusement increased. 'All right, then, ask me nicely to move and I might consider it.'

Caution fought briefly with annoyance and lost. 'Go to the devil!'

'You call that asking nicely?' He shook his head at her mockingly. 'You still have a lot to learn about handling men, green eyes. Now come over here and do it properly.'

If she didn't, Kim gathered from his tone, he was going to come and make her. She contemplated defying him anyway, but what was the use? At least if she went to him she retained some measure of initiative. Outwardly calm, she walked over to the bed and picked up the clean shirt lying across the foot, holding it out to him. 'Would you please put this on and clear out.'

For a big man he could move with lightning speed when he wanted to. Without moving from his reclining position he shot out a hand and pulled her down on to the bed at his side, leaning across her to stub out the cigarette in the tray on the side table. Grey eyes glinted down into green ones. 'You were saying?'

'You're crushing your shirt,' she said.

'So I find another.' His gaze slid over her features, rested a moment on the vulnerable hollow of her throat, then lifted again to her mouth. 'You're quivering,' he said. 'You're trying your damnedest not to let me know it, but you want me as much as I want you. And why not? We're both equipped with the same basic needs.'

'But a different set of values.' She tried to say it

steadily, to close her mind to the undeniable leaping of her own senses to his nearness. 'To you this says it all, doesn't it, Dave? Something totally physical. You couldn't care less what I'm thinking or feeling.'

His expression was curious. 'Do you care what *I'm* thinking or feeling at this moment?'

'No,' she returned promptly, 'because I don't care about you! That's what I'm talking about. For a man it could be any woman, providing he finds her reasonably attractive, but for a woman there has to be something more than that, some deeper feeling, before she can truly respond.'

The strong mouth curled. 'Like the kind of feeling you had for Adams, for instance? Now, he was something really special!' He watched her hand clench involuntarily into a fist and smiled narrowly. 'You do and you'll get more than you bargained for!'

For a brief pulsating moment Kim was tempted to risk it anyway for the sheer satisfaction of driving her knuckles into that cruel mouth, but only for a moment. Whatever satisfaction she might gain from hitting out at him, it would be more than cancelled out by the humiliation of what he would do to her in return. She relaxed into the pillows again, eyes blazing up at him. 'Leave Chris out of it!'

'Why?' he demanded. 'Because it still hurts to think of him down there with Mai, or because your pride can't stand the thought of having been wrong about him all the way down the line?'

Her throat closed up. 'I just don't want to talk about him.'

'Fine, so we'll forget him and concentrate on the here and now. Are you intent on keeping up the iceberg act, or are you going to start being honest with yourself?'

'Does it make any difference?'

'To me very little, to you a great deal. However much you rail against it you're stuck with me, so why not make the best of it?' His voice softened a fraction. 'Forget those high-flown principles of yours, green eyes. I'll take care of you.'

Her senses were melting, fusing together in exquisite sensation, but some small part of her clung on grimly to sanity.

'I won't give in to you, Dave,' she said thickly. 'Anything you want from me you're going to have to take.'

Impatience clouded his eyes and hardened his mouth again. 'If that's the way you want it to be.'

It was the way it was going to be, Kim told herself fiercely as his mouth claimed hers. No matter what it took she would never give him the satisfaction of knowing just how far he had brought her from the naïve girl he had married.

They reached Freetown about four o'clock on the Saturday afternoon, driving straight to the hotel Dave normally stayed at on his weekends in the town. Their room was clean and neat but unpretentious, the adjoining bathroom one of the smallest Kim had ever seen. Dave hoisted the suitcase on to one of the beds and watched her move across to the window with a edged smile on his lips.

'Too far to jump, or not far enough—depends how you look at it.'

Kim ignored him, gazing seawards. There were ships in the harbour. Maybe even a British vessel. Not that it would be any use to her if there were. Even if she had the money she would never get away from Dave for long enough to take advantage of it. Three more weeks, she thought. Three more weeks of being Mrs Dave Nelson, and then she could go home and never see him again. But never forget him either, a small voice whispered at the back of her mind, and she turned back abruptly into the room.

'What time is dinner?' she asked.

'Any time you want it,' he returned. 'Hungry?'

'No, just checking.' She clicked open the suitcase and took out her own things, hanging up the dress she had brought with her to wear that evening, together with a crisp gingham shirt for the morning. Her toilet things she put on the dressing table, then she turned back to the case and hesitated. 'Do you prefer to unpack for yourself?'

His shrug was easy. 'Be my guest. I'm going to find a drink. The bar is on the left as you come down the stairs if you feel like joining me when you're ready.'

'I'd sooner stay here, thanks,' she rejoined coolly.

'Okay.' He sounded indifferent. 'See you in a couple of hours.'

Left alone, Kim finished unpacking, hanging the fawn tropical worsted away in the cupboard provided. Dave's departure should have been a relief, yet without his presence overshadowing, the room seemed bare and empty. Almost, she began to regret having refused his invitation to join him downstairs. It had been a futile gesture anyway.

With the unpacking finished the next two hours stretched flatly ahead. Kim contemplated taking herself out for a look around the town in the immediate vicinity of the hotel, but the idea lacked appeal. The humidity was even higher down here than it had been at the mine, but at least the slowly revolving fan in the ceiling of the room kept it at a tolerable level.

She was looking out of the window again when the knock came on the door. She went to open it, staring blankly for an endless moment at the man standing there in the corridor before finally finding her voice.

'Chris!'

'Hallo, Kim.' His voice was low and edgy, his quick glance down the corridor behind him suggestive of nervousness. 'Can I come inside?'

'I . . .' Her voice felt caught up in her throat. She tried again. 'What do you want?'

'To talk to you.' There was an element of desperation in his eyes. 'Please, Kim, I'm in trouble. Real trouble!'

She stood back to let him into the room, closed the door and stood with her back against it. 'How did you know I was here?'

'I saw you arrive with Dave Nelson.' Now that he was in the room he seemed to feel safer, the nervousness giving way to speculation as his gaze slid over her. 'I waited till he came down again and went into the bar, then I dashed the receptionist to give me your room number. I've got to hand it to you. Dave Nelson is quite a catch. How did you manage it?'

'You might say I was lucky,' she retorted. 'What

did you mean just now, Chris? What kind of trouble are you in?'

He crossed to the window and peered down into the street below, twitched the blind back into place and turned back to look at her, hands sliding into his pockets in a gesture that was somehow defensive. 'Mai's husband is out to get me—him and her brother.'

'Get you?'

'Do me over. They came to the house this morning and took Mai away while I was out, then lay in wait for me. I'd have walked right into it if one of the street kids hadn't warned me.'

Kim gazed at him in confusion. 'How can I help you?' she queried at length.

'Well...' He hesitated. 'Have you any money?'

'Money?' She wanted suddenly to laugh. 'Chris, it's hardly any time ago that you told me you had enough to keep you going as long as it mattered.'

'So I thought.' His tone was wry. 'What's left was in the house. Knowing Mai like I do, that's the first thing she'd have thought of before she let herself be taken out of there. We were going to do a flit, you see, so I'd drawn every penny to my account in cash ready for the trip. I can't even go back there for a change of clothes until the heat's died off—and that's always providing they leave me anything. I've got about twenty pounds on me, and that's it.' He glanced at her curiously. 'What did you say?'

Kim gathered herself. 'It isn't important. I'm afraid I haven't any money either. Not the kind you would want.'

'You could get it, though.' He said it softly, insinuatingly. 'Any woman who could get Dave Nelson to marry her could get any man to do anything she wanted ... assuming that wasn't just a story you gave at the desk for the sake of appearances?'

'No, it wasn't, as a matter of fact.' Kim wondered how she could sound so calm about all this when her mind was in such a turmoil. 'But you're wrong about Dave. He wouldn't give me any money. And if he knew you were here he'd probably save Mai's husband a job. I'm ... sorry, Chris.'

'But you're my only hope!' The desperation was back in his eyes and in his voice. He crossed the space between them in a couple of long strides and took her by the shoulders, looking into her face with drawn appeal. 'Kim, you've got to help me! These people wouldn't think twice about maiming a man for life over a thing like this. I know I've been a fool, but try to understand. I couldn't help myself over Mai, though God knows I tried to stay away from her. She got me to such a pitch that I couldn't think straight any more. I had to have her, Kim. I had to!'

'Don't.' She was trembling. 'I don't want to know about her. You chose her instead of me. Why should you expect me to help you now?'

'Because of what we once were to one another. Because you're you, and I know you won't just stand by and see me get it.'

There was a lengthy pause before she said huskily, 'How much will you need?'

'Enough to get me on a ship out of here and stake me for a few days till I get fixed up with something. A couple of hundred should do it.' He saw her change of expression, added hastily, 'Well, a hundred anyway. I can't go anywhere on less than that.'

'You might have to.' Kim moved out of his grasp, conscious only of the need to get him out of the room. With no idea at all of how she was going to tackle the problem of procuring that kind of money, she added, 'Where can I contact you?'

'I'll have to stay around this place. I daren't be seen out on the streets again. I've taken a room down the corridor for tonight, but I'll have to be away tomorrow.'

Kim didn't think the time element was going to make much difference. Not in this particular case. No story she could concoct was going to satisfy Dave as a reason for giving her the money. The only way out was to tell him the truth, and she could imagine his reaction to that. But Chris had been right when he stated that she couldn't leave him in such a predicament. Which meant that she had to find a way of persuading Dave to oblige.

Throat tight and dry, she nodded. 'All right. You'd better go now.'

'Thanks.' He sounded as if he really meant it. 'I knew I could count on you, Kim.' With one hand on the door handle, he paused, his eyes going over her face. 'I must seem a real rat to you.'

'No.' She said it without any kind of expression. 'Just go, will you, before Dave comes up and finds you in here. I doubt that he'd wait for explanations.'

He went without further delay, leaving her to stand there gazing numbly at the closed door for a long moment before moving slowly across to sink to a seat on the bed edge. There was only one possible way to tackle this problem, and even that wasn't forced to work. But she was bound to try it because there was nothing else.

She had already changed into the blue tricel when Dave returned. She greeted him unemotionally, pretending to read a magazine while he showered and dressed again in the fawn suit. It was the first time she had seen him wearing anything more formal than a shirt and tie, and she had to admit that the suit made a difference. Gone was the tough outdoor man she was used to, and in his place stood a well-groomed stranger, cufflinks gleaming at the end of crisp shirt sleeves, body subtly fined down by smooth tailoring; even his features seemed somehow less angular. Only the grey eyes remained the same, flicking a mocking glance over her as she came reluctantly to her feet on his intimation that they should go downstairs.

'Try a smile,' he advised. 'We don't want everyone to think we're incompatible.'

'You couldn't care less what they might think,' she returned on a husky note, and he inclined his head.

'No, well, perhaps you're right. Shall we go?'

The dining room was full when they got there. Despite the fans revolving in the ceiling the atmosphere was hot and stuffy, and the flies were everywhere.

'The food's good, though,' Dave volunteered, watching Kim's face as she looked about her. 'In Africa you learn not to take too much notice of the surroundings.' He lit her cigarette and then his own from the candle stuck into an empty wine bottle, sitting back to regard her in the flickering glow. 'Enjoy your nap?'

Kim's head jerked. 'Nap?'

'I assume that's what you were doing while I was having a drink.' His gaze had sharpened a little. 'You didn't go out?'

'No. No, I didn't go out.' Her eyes went round the room again a little desperately. 'The service could be quicker.'

'There's no hurry,' he said. and paused. 'Or is there?'

She looked back at him swiftly. 'Why should there be?'

'Never answer a question with a question,' he advised softly. 'It always makes it seem that you might have something to hide.'

This was possibly the time to ask what she had to ask of him, but hardly the place. She looked away again, unaware that her fingers were nervously twisting the stem of her glass until he reached over and removed it from her hand. His own hand came back to imprison hers, holding it palm down on the cloth between them. Kim stared at it, feeling the steely strength of his fingers curving over the ball of her thumb, ready to grip and crush.

'*Do* you have anything to hide, Kim?' he asked with emphasis.

The moment was definitely ripe, but she still could not bring herself to take it. Chris was right here in the hotel. If Dave knew that there was no telling what he might do—especially if he knew that the other man had actually been with her in their room. And yet to conceal that fact now was only storing up trouble for later on.

'There's something I have to ask you,' she said at last with difficulty. 'Only not here, Dave. Let's have dinner first.'

It seemed an age before he answered, and his eyes seemed to bore into her. 'All right,' he agreed finally, 'so we'll eat first.'

Kim tasted little of the food put in front of her over the following hour, although she forced herself to eat it. Outwardly Dave showed no sign of impatience at her slowness, but she was aware of a certain tension in the line of his jawbone when he caught her gaze. Intuitively she sensed that he knew her behaviour had something to do with Chris, and that he was exercising great control in not demanding the truth of the matter here and now. It was her own fault, of course. Had she possessed greater control herself he would not have guessed that anything was wrong at all until she chose to tell him. As it was, the moment they were out of this place he was going to make certain that she came clean with what was bothering her, and heaven only knew where he would take matters from there.

As it turned out she was wrong in her estimate of Dave's forbearance. The meal over, he took her out of the hotel into the lively street crowded with stalls lit by pressure lamps, and before she knew where she was they were in the car and driving away from the town. Freetown has an enormous prison on both sides of the main road. To Kim the electrified walls seemed to stretch for miles, grim and forbidding. She was thankful when at last they left them behind and drove on beside the sea in the hot, humid darkness, preferring even the nerve-racking tension of being completely alone with Dave to the sheer depressive quality of those high prison walls.

Eventually they came to a long beach with a golf course alongside. Dave brought the car to a stop on the grass and switched off the engine, reaching for the inevitable cigarette.

'Right,' he said. 'Spill it.'

This was the Dave she knew. No leading up to the point, but straight to it. Kim moved a little further into the corner of her seat and wondered how to start—or more precisely, at which point. How did one go about striking the kind of bargain she was contemplating?

'Chris is in trouble,' she said at length.

'I gathered that.' The words were brusquely spoken. 'Nemesis caught up with him at last, has it?'

'I suppose you might call it that.' She shivered a little despite the heat. 'Would they really ... harm him if they caught up with him?'

'If by they you mean Mai's husband and brother, they'd certainly make sure he didn't go around stealing any other man's wife for a long time,' he returned dryly. 'People here lack our civilised Western ways when it comes to affairs of this nature. They believe in an eye for an eye.'

'But he wasn't entirely to blame,' she protested. 'Mai went with him.'

'That's beside the point.' He moved his position, turning his head so that he could see her face. 'I suppose he wants money.'

Kim caught her lip between her teeth. 'Yes.'

'And he expects you to get it for him, obviously?

From me?'

'Yes,' she said again.

The pause was unnerving. 'What reason might he have for thinking I'd be willing to finance his getaway?'

'No reason. Only'—she searched desperately for some way to say it—'only that we're married, and he thought...'

'And he thought that having given you so much I could probably refuse you nothing,' he continued for her inexorably as her voice petered out. 'Naturally you didn't enlighten him as to our arrangement, but I'd have thought you knew me better by now than to expect me to oblige. That ex-fiancé of yours deserves everything that's coming to him, and I wouldn't personally lift a finger to help him.'

Kim curled her hands into her lap. 'I'd ... pay you back.'

The lift of his brow was sensed rather than seen. 'How?'

The next was the most difficult thing she had ever had to say in her life. 'I'd be ... what you wanted.'

It was difficult to gauge his reaction from his expression, but when he did speak there was nothing uncertain about his tone. 'You mean you'd sell yourself out for the price of Adams's safety.'

'If you want to see it that way.'

'What other way is there to see it?' He crushed the glowing tip of the cigarette between finger and thumb and tossed it into the darkness with vicious force. 'I'd have reckoned on you having enough pride to tell him to go to the devil for all you cared about him after what he did to you.'

What Chris had done to her was as nothing compared with the methods of some, she thought, but refrained from voicing that particular sentiment. 'I don't care about him,' she said. 'Not in the way you mean. But neither can I just sit back and ignore the fact that he needs help. If there was any other way of getting him the money...' She paused there, not looking at him. 'It hardly seemed likely that you'd offer your help without compensation.'

'I wasn't aware that I had offered it yet,' he came back with cruel inflection. 'Just what is it I'm supposed to get in return?'

Kim drew in a painful breath. 'I'm sure I don't have to spell it out for you.'

'No,' he agreed after a moment, 'I don't suppose you do.' His hand came out suddenly, taking her chin and bringing her face round towards him. His own was hard. 'Only let's get this thing in perspective, shall we. You're not making any sacrifices, Kim. What you're promising me is only what you've been wanting to give since the first time I made love to you. Still, if it soothes your ideals to tell yourself that you're doing it for Adams, go right ahead. I shan't mind *what* you tell yourself providing I find a real woman instead of a girl.'

With his lips hard and demanding on hers there was suddenly no room to tell herself anything any more. After days of holding her emotions in check the relief of at last letting go was infinite and sensational. As if of their own accord her arms slipped up and about his neck, her fingers weaving into the springing thickness of his hair. She felt his arms tightening across her back, the hardness of his chest crushing the breath from her, the need she had denied welling up inside her like a spring. When he put her abruptly and none too gently away from him it was like a douche of cold water in the face. Limbs quivering, she sat there in the darkness gazing at him, sensing the change in his mood without understanding it.

'Dave?' It was a whisper, tentative, questioning. Only then did he move, turning his body to reach out and start the engine.

'Don't worry,' he said harshly. 'Adams will get his money. Only after this I don't want to hear his name mentioned again. Clear?'

Kim didn't answer. There was no answer necessary. What she had begun to hope for during those few emotional moments she wasn't quite certain, but whatever it was Dave's attitude now was more than enough to kill it. There was no softness in him at all. A bargain had been struck, and that was all it meant to him. She could tell herself that that was all it meant to her too, only she would know deep down that it wasn't wholly true. She only wished to heaven that it were.

CHAPTER SIX

DAVE insisted on seeing Chris alone the following morning, taking himself off to the other man's room as soon as he was dressed. It was more than two hours before he returned. Two hours during which Kim sat tensely by the window watching the street down which the two men had disappeared. Where Dave was going to get hold of a fairly large sum of money at this hour on a Sunday morning she had no idea, and had not cared to ask. All she did know was that there was an overwhelming relief in the sight of the tall, strong figure coming back along the colourful thoroughfare.

She was folding the dress she had worn the previous evening back into the case when he entered the room. She looked at him quickly and away again, not quite sure enough of herself to ask the question trembling on her lips.

'He's on a boat to Dakar,' Dave proffered shortly. 'And that, with any luck, is the last we'll see of him. Have you had breakfast?'

Kim shook her head. 'I waited for you.'

'Thoughtful of you. We'll get off to the beach straight afterwards. If we take some food with us we can spend the day there and just come back here for dinner before going back home.' He flicked a satirical eyebrow at the expression which flitted briefly across her face. 'It may not seem much of one to you, but it's the only one *I've* known for the last three years. Let's go and eat.'

The meal was a strained one, with Dave making no effort at all to dispel the atmosphere which lay between them like something almost tangible. Outside, everyone seemed to be on their way to church, some dressed soberly in black with solemn expressions, the majority colourful, gay and laughing. There was languor in the air, the serene, unhurried pace of all tropical towns. Grass grew in the wide main streets shaded with cassais, and occasionally bright orange lizards darted across them. Down both sides of the streets ran deep gutters two feet wide which became swirling rivers when it rained.

They drove to the same beach they had visited the night before, crowded now with a variety of nationalities. Kim shook her head when Dave suggested a swim, saying she would go in later on. She watched him move off towards the water's edge, quick to note the way in which other heads turned as he passed. Even among so many he stood out, drawing feminine attention without trying.

He seemed more relaxed when he returned, flinging himself down on the sand beside her and reaching for cigarettes.

'You should have come in,' he said. 'It's grand.' He swung an inquiring glance her way. 'You do swim?'

Kim acknowledged the fact that she did, if not particularly well, and thought how little the two of them actually knew about one another. They were married, living together as man and wife, and yet they were still to all intents and purposes total strangers. She supposed it was better that way. When the time came to finally part there would be that much less to forget—if she ever could forget.

'You haven't forgotten your promise to let me have a car when we got back to the mine?' she asked after a moment.

'I haven't forgotten.' His eyes were closed, his tone almost indulgent. 'The practice will be useful for later on.'

'Later on?'

'When the job finishes.' He still didn't open his eyes. 'I've decided to take a bit of a trip before heading back to England. Perhaps go south and pick up a boat in Lagos.'

Kim was very still, the sand she had been trickling through her fingers settling into the cupped palm of her hand. 'You ... intend taking me with you?'

'Naturally.' He said it without undue emphasis. 'What else would I do with you?'

'You could always put me on a boat for home on my own,' she said.

Grey eyes came open to study her slightly averted face. 'Is that what you'd prefer?'

Was it what she would prefer? Kim couldn't for the life of her find an immediate answer. On the one hand was freedom and home, and on the other an extension, perhaps stretching into weeks, of association with a man who had no feeling for her beyond the physical desire which must itself eventually fade.

'Do I really have a choice?' she queried, and saw a smile slowly stretch the corners of his mouth.

'No, you don't. Not at this point. We have...'

'So this is what's been keeping you away, Dave.' The voice came from behind them. Kim looked round swiftly at the thickset man in bathing trunks who loomed over them, and met an openly appraising pair of pale blue eyes which made her feel a bit like a fish wriggling on the end of a spear. 'Can't say that I blame you for wanting to keep her to yourself,' he went on. 'But now that I'm here you can't do less than introduce us.'

Dave had come to a sitting position, his expression as enigmatic as only he knew how to make it. 'Kim, meet Ralph Tait,' he said, and then still without a flicker of expression. 'My wife.'

Kim had often read the phrase "his jaw dropped", but she had never before seen it actually happen in real life. To say that the newcomer was surprised would have been something of an understatement. but his recovery was fast.

'Now I've heard everything,' he stated. 'Dave Nelson tied up at last!' The pale blue eyes flickered over Kim once more, reassessing first impressions. 'You're going to be pretty unpopular in certain quarters, I can tell you. There's been more than one tried to stake a claim on this man of yours. What's the secret?'

'Turn it up, Ralph.' Dave spoke quietly enough, but there was an edge to his voice. 'Are you on your own?'

'No.' The other inclined his head in the direction of the trees backing the beach. 'The others are further back. I was going for a dip when I spotted you.' His tone changed subtly. 'Karen's with us. Funny, she was only talking about you last night.'

'Was she?' The comment gave nothing away.

'Yes. Look'—Ralph obviously took no heed of hints—'you can't get away without at least saying hallo to everybody. Better still, how about joining us for lunch? You know how much stuff Bea always packs up. Plenty for all comers.'

'Actually, we've brought our own,' Kim put in hesitantly when Dave made no immediate reply.

'Better still. Bring it over and toss it in with the rest.' Ralph looked from her to Dave, eyes suddenly curious. 'Come on, man, the honeymoon can't last for ever. I'm sure Kim here would like to meet some of your ... friends.'

Dave heaved himself abruptly to his feet, dusting the sand off his damp trunks. He didn't look at Kim at all. 'Okay, tell them we're on our way as soon as we've got ourselves together.'

Kim began gathering up their various belongings as Ralph went off, aware of a certain tautness of Dave's stance. 'Who are these people?' she ventured when she was standing herself with her bag repacked. 'I mean, how did you meet them?'

'Ralph is in timber—employed on a consultant basis. I've spent one or two weekends with him and his wife. There's another couple who always run around with them.' He moved impatiently. 'Come on.'

The group awaited them under the shade of a clump of palms, their faces reflecting varying emotions as the newcomers approached. Kim's attention was drawn at once to the youngest woman in the party, a slim, shapely brunette in a bright yellow bikini whose smoothly tanned, classically-boned features were frankly speculative as she looked Kim up and down.

'Long time no see,' she said to Dave.

'So it is.' The reply was easy. 'Too long. How are things with you?'

'Dandy.' Her eyes came back to Kim again, an odd, almost amused expression in their tawny depths. 'How about introducing me to your wife?'

'No need for formality, is there?' One hand lightly on her shoulder, he brought Kim a step closer to his side. 'This is Karen; the lady with the hamper over there is Bea; Ralph you already know. Then we have Vida and Norris.' The hand increased its pressure, urging her forward a little into the group. 'Park yourself with the girls. They don't bite.'

Bea chuckled suddenly, a young sound which went oddly with her blue-rinsed hair and well controlled figure. She was probably in her mid-forties and prematurely grey, yet still with a few years' advantage over her husband. 'You know, I've missed you, Dave,' she said. 'You're the only man I know who can make an insult sound like a compliment.' The glance she gave Kim was a kindly one. 'You've taken something on with this one!'

'Perhaps Kim finds him easy to handle,' put in Karen smoothly. 'She looks capable. Do you?' The question was directed this time at Kim herself and demanded an answer of some kind.

Out of the corner of her eye, Kim could see Dave sitting with Norris a couple of feet away, and knew that her reply would be heard. 'I'm learning,' she said.

'How did you two meet?' Bea asked Dave. 'I thought you'd been stuck out at the mine for the last six weeks.'

'I have,' he answered casually. 'Kim has a job with the Company.'

'Didn't know they'd started importing women into mining,' said Ralph with some scepticism. 'Quite an improvement all round. You don't have much longer to go, do you?'

'No.' Dave made no attempt to enlarge on that statement.

'And meanwhile, you're living out at the mine?' Bea obviously regarded that state of affairs as something she could not have even dreamed of contemplating herself. 'My God, what we women do for love!'

Kim sensed the irony in Dave's regard and fought to keep the telltale colour at bay. If these people knew the truth of the matter they probably wouldn't believe it. Who would? No woman in her right mind would look at Dave and see the man *she* had imagined him to be for those few short hours.

If Dave enjoyed the following hour Kim certainly did not, although she did her best to act naturally. Karen had moved over to where he was sitting on the pretext of handing him more of the fried chicken, and had stayed right there beside him, talking animatedly of people and occasions of which Kim could have no knowledge. That there had been some kind of relationship between the two of them in the past was more than apparent. Kim tried not to allow her thoughts to dwell on the matter. It was nothing to do with her. Yet she couldn't help wondering at Karen's apparent lack of concern over the advent of a wife into Dave's life when she so obviously still found him vitally attractive herself. Had the positions been reversed she doubted that she could have retained quite the same poise and assurance in the face of things.

It was gone three when someone suggested a swim. Kim was one of the first on her feet, grateful for the excuse to get away from this increasingly difficult situation for a short time. Once in the water she put a little distance between herself and the others, swimming out towards the reef which jutted out into the sea from the right-hand curve of the bay with the intention of resting there for a few minutes alone.

It was further than she had realised. Before she had gone halfway she could feel the muscles in the back of her legs starting to ache, and her arms becoming leaden. She trod water for a moment or two to regain her breath, trying not to panic at the realisation that she was well and truly out of her depth in a sea which could hold all sorts of unknown terrors. The reef looked almost as far away as when she had set off, yet the beach seemed equally distant. She couldn't make it to either haven of safety, she thought in rising desperation. She would never have the strength.

The swimmer cutting through the water towards her was like a lifeline. She began to move towards him, forcing her limbs to answer the call for some co-ordination, although making little impression upon the distance between them herself. When Dave finally reached her she was only too ready to give herself over to his taut-lipped instructions, turning on her back with his arm hard across her chest as he drew her through the water. It seemed an age before she was able to put down her feet and feel the sand beneath them again, and even then Dave didn't let go of her completely, clamping an arm about her waist and almost lifting her through the shallows on to the beach itself. His own breathing was heavy, his chest rising and falling with gradually decreasing rapidity as he regarded her.

'What the devil did you think you were doing out there?' he demanded roughly. 'You said yourself that you weren't a strong swimmer, and then you deliberately go out of your depth! You deserve...' He stopped abruptly, expression still grim as the rest of the party came splashing over to where they stood.

'What happened?' asked Norris for them all. 'Cramp?'

'I—I just went a bit too far out, that's all,' Kim answered, controlling the tremors running through her body as well as she was able. 'I'm perfectly all right now.'

'You look as pale as death,' commented Bea in some concern. She looked at Dave. 'Perhaps it would be a good thing if you came back to the house and let her recover for a while. Shock can be a tricky thing.'

'It really isn't necessary,' Kim protested swiftly. 'And we have to go back to town for our things from the hotel.'

'We can always do that later,' put in Dave decisively. 'Bea's right. You've had a fright and should lie down. There'll be plenty of time to get back to town.' His hand came under her elbow. 'We'll take you up on that offer, Bea.'

'Tell you what,' said the other, falling into step

beside them. 'You could slip back to fetch your stuff yourself, Dave, and stay to dinner with us. After all, you're part way back to the mine already from this end.'

Don't. Kim wanted to say. Don't leave me here alone with these people. But Dave was already nodding his head.

'Good idea. I'll do that.'

The whole party adjourned to the cars. Alone in the Land-Rover with Dave, Kim said hollowly, 'I'd rather come back with you and have dinner at the hotel as we planned. I really am perfectly all right.'

His glance flicked briefly over her face. 'I'll believe that when your colour comes back. Anyway, I've already accepted the invitation.' He paused. 'Why the reluctance? I would have thought you'd be glad of some company other than mine.'

Her head came up a fraction. 'I haven't said that.'

'No.' His tone was dry. 'Look, like it or not we're having a meal with the Taits, so put a good face on it. I don't know what it is you've got against them, but...'

'It isn't so much the Taits,' she said without stopping to think about it. 'It's just that ... well, Karen will be there too, won't she?'

Dave's eyes narrowed against the sun. 'Where does she come into it?'

It was a moment before Kim answered that one. 'She's made it rather obvious that she's attracted to you,' she said at last.

'So?' His lips twisted. 'You're not trying to make out that you're jealous?'

'No, I'm not,' with some asperity, 'but I object to

being treated as if I were of absolutely no consequence. She may once have had some claim on you...'

The lean features were set in taut lines. 'Don't let your imagination run away with you. No woman has a claim on me—including you. If Karen treats you as you say that's your own fault. What do you expect me to do about it?'

'Not a thing.' There was more than just anger in the response which came jerking from her lips. 'I'll bet you're getting a real kick out of this whole situation. The way you've fixed things you can carry on affairs with any number of women without the least danger from any source. No wonder you want to extend our association. It's the perfect set-up for someone like you!'

'I think you'd better shut up,' he advised softly. 'You've said just about enough.'

Kim shut up. It would have been tempting providence not to have done so. Her nerves quivering, she gazed stonily ahead through the windscreen at the car they were following, conscious of the whiteness of Dave's knuckles curved about the wheel. There was a hard lump in her throat and a sense of constriction in her chest. Dave *had* had an affair with Karen, the tone of his reaction confirmed that much. So what? she asked herself numbly. What difference did it make? Dave had never tried to conceal his contempt for the whole of the female sex beyond a certain limit of usefulness, and Karen apparently merited no better opinion. Where was the point in feeling so choked up about it? Dave just wasn't worth any heartache on her part. He wasn't worth it!

The Tait home was in the hills some ten minutes' drive from the beach, a square, stone-built bunglow with the usual deep veranda running round three sides. Mango trees overhung the road leading to it, dark, densely leafed and loaded with fruit. Flowers gleamed like jewels among the undergrowth and in the cleared area of ground in front of the bungalow itself, yellow acacia mingling happily with the deep purple of guava and brassy African marigolds. The air was heavy with the scent of frangipani, palpable with heat, humidity and languor.

It was cooler indoors, the dimness of the bedroom to which Kim was shown a welcome relief. She had slipped on her beach robe over the wet swim suit, and roughly towelled her hair before leaving the beach without giving a thought to her appearance. Now, catching a glimpse of herself in the long mirror set into the door of the wardrobe, she gave a wry smile. She looked terrible, her hair hanging lankly about her shoulders, her face devoid of colour. Her head ached with a dull relentless throbbing. Perhaps Bea was right about shock taking its effect, although looking back on those few moments alone in the water it all seemed so silly now. There had been no danger. All she had had to do was to float on her back until she had recovered her breath enough to swim back to the beach. This was the second time Dave had been forced to rescue her from a situation caused entirely by her swiftness to panic, and this time he had quite definitely not been amused.

She was fastening the zip of the beige linen slacks when the door opened, Dave was carrying a cup and saucer in one hand and in the other a bottle of tablets.

'Tea and a sedative,' he said. 'It's only a little after four-thirty. I'd suggest that you try and have a nap on the bed while I'm in town.'

'I don't want a sedative,' Kim replied stubbornly. 'I'll lie down if you think it necessary, but there's nothing wrong with me that a shower wouldn't put right.'

'You can take a shower when I get back with your clothes,' he returned. He placed the tea on the bedside table and shook out a couple of the small white tablets into the palm of his hand, holding them out to her. 'These will calm you down. Right now you seem to need it.'

Green eyes clashed with grey and slid away. Without another word, Kim took the pills from him and put them both in her mouth, washed them down with a mouthful of the warm tea and lay down on the bed, averting her face from his gaze.

'I'll see you later,' he said, and was gone, the door closing softly behind him.

It was already dark outside when Kim awoke. She sat up, blinking in the glow of the table lamp someone had switched on. The blue dress lay neatly over the back of one chair, while on the other rested the opened suitcase. The bedroom door was still closed, but from somewhere in the house she could hear faint voices, and then a woman's tinkling laugh.

Her watch said seven o'clock. She pushed back the hair out of her eyes. The headache had gone and she felt infinitely more herself again. Capable, at least, of facing the rest of this interminably long day. Just dinner to get through, and then it would be time to leave for the mine. Right at this moment she could hardly wait to get back.

Bea had informed her that the bathroom was next door but one. Kim slipped out of the crumpled slacks and shirt and into the blue wrap, then went to find it. There was no one in the tiled hall; the voices were coming from the direction of the living room at the far end. She recognised Ralph's confident tones—and that was Vida, she thought, answering him. She wondered where Dave was, and how long he had been back. He must have been very quiet when he had brought in the suitcase. Either that, or the pills she had taken had deadened her senses completely during the two and a half hours she had slept.

The shower brought her back on an even keel again. She would have liked to wash her hair too, but had to make do with a quick freshen up with cologne. Back in the bedroom she put on her dress and slid her feet into the white sandals which went with it, applied make-up sparingly and ran a brush over her hair before fastening it back into her nape. Apart from a certain darkness under her eyes she looked normal enough. Resolutely she turned her back on the mirror and made her way out of the room to join the others.

The first thing she saw on entering the comfortably furnished living room was Dave standing over by a potted date tree with Karen. The lovely brunette had a hand resting on his sleeve and was speaking in low tones, a smile on her face. Dave looked tolerant and expansive as if he were suddenly finding life very good.

'Hallo there,' exclaimed Bea, spotting Kim hovering uncertainly in the doorway. 'Feeling better?'

Kim nodded and forced a smile. 'Yes, thanks. I must have been tired. I slept for ages.'

'Yes, Dave said you were still unconscious when he went to get changed. He thought it would be best to leave you to wake naturally, so we've arranged that you should both spend the night here and travel back to the mine first thing in the morning. No reason why the arrangement shouldn't stand, of course. It will do you good to spend a night in a civilised bed. Do come and sit down, dear. Ralph will get you a drink.'

'What will you have?' inquired her husband from behind the bamboo bar built into a corner of the room.

Dave was watching her. Even from here she could feel his steady regard on her, but she refused to glance in his direction. 'Gin, please,' she said with deliberation.

'Anything in it?'

'Just ice.'

Ralph lifted heavy brows and grinned. 'A woman after my own heart. Never drown good spirit!' He brought the glass across to her, half full of the colourless liquid. 'Down the hatch.'

Already regretting the childish defiance, Kim took a cautious sip and had to fight not to allow her reactions to show in her expression. Without the stronger taste of the lime to overshadow it the stuff was horrible. How on earth was she going to drink the rest of it without giving herself away to everyone in the room?

She could have blessed Norris when he distracted Ralph's attention from her with a query about his job. Momentarily unobserved, she put the glass down on the table beside her chair and sat back with what she hoped was a casual air, fixing a smile on her face as the conversation flowed about her. Dave loomed unexpectedly at her side, perching casually on the arm of her chair and leaning an arm along the back behind her head. She was intensely aware of his nearness, and knew a sudden and desperate longing to be closer. It was no use denying the effect he had on her senses. No woman could hope to remain indifferent to a man like Dave. Even hating him as she did, she ... Her thoughts paused there. Hate? Was that really what she meant? Was it possible to still hate the man in whose arms she had discovered a whole new range of emotions?

Karen was seated directly opposite. Meeting the confident, tawny eyes, Kim felt the sense of inadequacy creeping over her again. Without allowing herself to think about it first, she put her head back slowly until it rested against Dave's arm, turning her cheek a little so that it just brushed his sleeve. Just as easily his hand slid down the chair back to her shoulder and stayed there, his very touch possessive in a way which only a few days ago would have roused her bitterest resentment. She was leaving herself wide open to misinterpretation, yet she couldn't bring herself to care at the moment. No matter why, or for how long, she was Dave's wife *now*, and it was time Karen realised it.

Whether by accident or faintly malicious design on Bea's part, seating arrangements at dinner

144

found Dave placed between Kim on one hand and Karen on the other. With her attention only half claimed by her host's conversational offerings, Kim kept picking up snatches of what the other two were discussing, and was forced to acknowledge that the older woman seemed at ease with Dave in a way which she herself could never be. She stood no chance of ever understanding a woman of Karen's type, she realised. Nothing appeared to disconcert her. In many ways she envied her that command over emotion.

They had coffee back in the living room. Kim took hers over to a chair by the door and sat looking out at the cricket-filled night. She could smell the sickly sweetness of mango fruit fallen from the trees and left to rot on the ground, interlaced with perfumes of orange and pineapple borne on the sultry breeze coming up from the valley. Faintly and far away there was a throbbing of drums, subtly underlining the unchangeableness of Africa and her peoples.

Ralph came over to join her, perching on the arm of her chair much as Dave had done earlier. 'You know, you intrigue me, Kim,' he said softly. 'You're such a bundle of contradictions. On the surface you appear so calm and well balanced, then you suddenly do something capricious, like asking for a drink you don't even like. And just now when you looked up at me you had an expression in your eyes like green flames before you put the shields up again. What gives with you?'

'Nothing of importance.' she replied on a light note. 'I'm sorry about the gin. It was rather silly of me. Perhaps I could have some lime in it after we've finished coffee?'

'I'm not concerned about the gin,' he said. 'I'm talking about *you*. What I'd really like to know is how you got out here in the first place.'

'Dave already told you,' she began, and received a derisive snort by way of reply.

'I know what Dave told us—and he's lying through his teeth. No mining company in these parts would take a woman on their payroll—especially one who looks like you do! It would be spelling out trouble with a capital T!'

'But I am. I am on their payroll. I do the wages sheets.'

Ralph regarded her narrowly for a long moment, before smiling and shaking his head. 'Now, maybe. As Dave Nelson's wife you'd be a different proposition. The rest doesn't stand up.' He paused again. 'I notice you don't wear a ring.'

'No. We ... never got around to getting one.' It was none of his business, but suddenly Kim didn't care. Let him have the truth, up to a point. 'As a matter of fact, I came to Africa looking for my fiancé, only to find that he'd got himself another girl. So I married Dave instead.'

'Just like that?' There was a certain admiration in his gaze. 'You certainly didn't waste time in sorting out your priorities. You're quite a girl, Kim!'

Her heart jerked. 'Don't you want any more coffee?'

'There's plenty.' Ralph obviously had no intention of dropping the inquisition prematurely. 'Do you think you'll be able to hang on to him?'

Kim turned her face slightly away. 'I'm his wife.'

'That doesn't give you much protection in this

country. Best thing you can do is get him back to England as soon as possible. At least there you'd have some claim on him if anything goes wrong.'

Was it so obvious to everyone that Dave didn't love her? she wondered numbly. It certainly seemed apparent to Ralph that the relationship had a temporary air about it.

'I never cross bridges before I come to them,' she said with her chin lifted. 'May I have some more of that coffee going spare?'

Karen was sitting with Dave on the long lounger, fingers resting lightly on his knee as she emphasised some point. Ralph would no doubt tell her the story so far as he knew it as soon as he got the opportunity. Not that it would make any difference to the other woman's attitude. She seemed already to take it for granted that Dave's marriage presented no problems which time would not solve. Kim wondered if she knew that Dave had no plans to return to Sierra Leone after his trip home to England.

It was Dave who broke up the evening eventually by pleading an early start. In their room, he took off his jacket and hung it up and was unfastening his cufflinks before he said casually, 'You and Ralph were getting very cosy in the corner a bit back. What was his game?'

'He just wanted to talk,' Kim answered.

'About what?'

She slid the ribbon out of her hair and shook it free. 'Us.'

He was watching her in the mirror. 'What did you tell him?'

'The truth.' She said it with slight defiance.

'Ralph is no fool. He'd already guessed that we don't have a proper marriage.'

Dave's grin was as sudden as it was unexpected. 'What's improper about it?'

The zip of her dress was stuck. Kim tugged at it viciously, said bitingly, 'It may be a joking matter to you, but I can't find anything humorous in being regarded as one step from a ... a kept woman!'

'Wives *are* kept women, mostly. It's a fact of life.' He had come up behind her. 'Stop yanking at it like that, you're going to tear the material.'

'Well, fine—you can buy me another.' She felt his fingers moving at her nape, the tingle of awareness his touch always kindled. Her chest tight, she said huskily, 'Dave, what you said earlier about not going straight back to England when your job here finishes...'

'You're coming with me. I told you that too.' His tone was unequivocal. 'I'll take you back to England when I'm good and ready, so if you're thinking of suggesting anything else don't waste your time.'

She could see him in the mirror, reflected behind her, tall, massive-shouldered, taut-featured. Husband; lover; enigma still. Don't waste your time asking me to let you go, he had said, so she wouldn't. From now on she would live each day as it came, and to the devil with the future. Whatever happened eventually she was wanted now by someone, and that was all she was going to allow to matter.

CHAPTER SEVEN

LIFE followed much the same pattern out at the mine over the next couple of weeks. They worked, and ate and slept, then woke again to the same routine. For Kim, however, the acquisition of the promised car held out welcome possibilities. The first thing she did after Dave handed over the keys was to take a drive around the site, although the previous day's rain made that a sticky proposition.

With the help of some memorised recipes and a little ingenuity, she managed some improvment on the standard of Patrick's cooking. He was quite happy to have her practically take over the evening meal while he just pottered about laying the table, and completely in accord with her desire to keep the extent of her culinary activities from the boss, even if he didn't understand the reason for it. After all, this way he got the credit without having to do the work.

It was Friday night when Kim tentatively suggested having Luke and a couple of the other engineers over for a meal the following evening.

'It would make a change from the club,' she pointed out. 'Luke was only saying the other day that another one of Sing's chocolate puddings would finish him off altogether.'

'He's been saying that since he got here.' Dave studied her speculatively as she leaned against the veranda rail. 'It sounds almost too civilised for our way of life—quite apart from the fact that we don't happn to be able to equal up the numbers. Or were you rather fancying the thought of being one woman to four men?'

'I've often been that in the clubhouse,' she reminded him, determined not to allow him to rile her. 'And I see no reason why we can't be civilised just because there's a shortage of partners. If you want a reason for inviting them you could always make it the preliminary to a poker game. I'd already thought of Carl Gerhardt as one of the party.'

'You seem to be thinking of everything,' he said with an unwonted edge. 'Suppose they've all planned on going into town this weekend?'

'They haven't. I checked.' Having got this far Kim was not going to be put off easily. 'Is it on then?'

Dave picked up one of the new batch of magazines which had come in recently and opened it at random. 'Do as you like.'

So far as appreciation of her cooking went, Kim supposed she could call the dinner party a qualified success, but it was obvious that all four men found the unaccustomed formality of the occasion somewhat off-putting. Ties were the general rule in the clubhouse at weekends, but rarely worn anywhere else. Sitting there at the table in the small living room, hot and uncomfortable in tropical suits, the four of them looked as out of place as a bunch of hippies in the Ritz restaurant. Kim wished that she had thought to stipulate a casual appearance, although they probably would not have taken any notice. She had set the standard by arranging this affair in the first place.

It was only after the cigars and brandy that the three visitors began to show signs of relaxing, and Dave's suggestion that they should play a few hands of poker met with a ready response. Within minutes they were all totally at ease, jackets slung over chair backs, ties loosened, sleeves rolled up. Forgotten, Kim attempted to read a book for a while, curled up in a chair by the door, but the murmur of voices, the heat and the smoke, made concentration difficult if not impossible. She didn't think any of them noticed when she got up quietly and went outside for some air.

There had been one of the typical flash storms in the late afternoon. Mud puddles lay everywhere, while the air itself was thick with the smell of sodden vegetation. A sticky wind kept lifting the roof of the veranda at the far corner where it had worked loose. If something wasn't done about that soon it would all start to go. Kim supposed that Dave had little interest in what happened to the place once he had left it. It would be up to the next occupier to have repairs seen to.

She had been standing there for about five minutes when she heard the vehicle coming down the track from the direction of the club. It hove into view with headlights blazing, avoiding the worst of the water-filled ruts to swerve to a halt in front of the steps.

'Got some visitors for you,' called the driver, stepping out into the mud. He put both hands about the waist of the young woman who had been sitting beside him in front, and swung her easily across to the steps, releasing her with obvious reluctance. 'You'll be all right now, miss.'

Kim stirred herself to move as another figure leapt the distance between car and veranda; male this time, and young.

'Hallo, Karen,' she said tonelessly. 'This is ... quite a surprise.'

'Isn't it?' The other ruefully examined the ruin of her slacks by the light of the pressure lamp before lifting her head to meet Kim's gaze. A smile came suddenly to her lips, a hint of malice in it. 'I'd have thought shock might be a better word. Is Dave inside?'

'Half and half.' He had come to the door, drawn by the voices. As usual it was hard to tell what he was thinking. He simply stood there in the doorway with one hand resting on the jamb, regarding the newcomers with faintly raised brows but no astonishment. 'A bit of an odd time to come visiting,' he added.

'We'd have been here hours ago if it hadn't been for the storm,' profferred the man at Karen's side hurriedly. 'We set off right after lunch.'

'The road's washed out, Dave,' put in the driver who had brought them here, tearing his gaze away from Karen. 'I found them at the head of the gully. Their own car's stuck.'

'Austin's skilful handling.' Karen said it derisively, drawing a flush to the face of her companion. 'He was supposed to be turning it round to take us back when we found the road had collapsed.'

'I hit a fissure and got a wheel stuck.' The explanation was defensive. 'The way it was raining I couldn't see a thing.'

'You'd have been better sitting it out until you could, then,' came the blunt comment from Dave. 'You'd better both come inside.' His glance moved to Kim. 'Tell Pat we'll need hot water, will you?'

'Wouldn't they be better getting cleaned up at the club?' she suggested hesitantly. 'It's difficult out at the back when you're not used to it.'

'They'll manage,' he returned evenly. 'You might look out a change of clothes for Karen while you're about it. I'll find something for our other guest.'

Karen laughed. 'I haven't introduced you, have I? His name is Moyes. Austin, meet Dave Nelson— oh, and this is Kim.'

The other three poker players were on their feet when they got indoors. With seven people in it the room seemed even pokier than usual, the furnishings totally inadequate. Karen took one brief glance round without bothering to conceal her disparagement, looking back at Dave with a smiling lift of her shoulders.

'We seem to have broken up a party.'

Luke said hastily, 'We'll be pushing off, Dave. You'll need to organise some beds. Want me to call in at the club?'

'If you would.'

Goodnights were said, and Dave accompanied the three engineers out to the front step. Kim murmured something about hot water and clean clothes, and went through to the kitchen to tell Patrick that he had by no means finished work for the night. In the bedroom she sorted out a newly laundered pair of slacks and a clean shirt, then stood for a moment with them in her hand, trying to sort out her own emotions. Karen's coming here to the mine didn't necessarily mean that Dave had suggested the visit. On the contrary, he had quite obviously not been expecting to see her standing there on his step. But that didn't mean that he wasn't glad to see her either. He had been so withdrawn this last week or two, like a man with something—or someone—on his mind. Maybe seeing Karen again the other weekend had made him realise just how much he had been attracted to her. It would be just like him to feign indifference under the circumstances. On the other hand, if that were true he would hardly be continuing with his plans to take her, Kim, on this trip down the coast with him, would he?

Bleakly, she had to acknowledge that where Dave was concerned nothing was a certainty.

Karen accepted the clean clothing with the air of one who had to make the best of things regardless. Kim took her out to the back and showed her how to work the shower, fully anticipating the other's reactions.

'It's a bit utilitarian,' she agreed, 'but it does work all right. I'll fetch you my wrap so you can dress in the bedroom when you're through.'

'Well, I'm certainly not doing it out here,' was the prompt reply. 'Heaven only knows what might be crawling around in there!'

For a moment Kim wondered whether to warn her about scorpions, but decided against it. Patrick was under instructions to inspect the interior of the enclosure before announcing it ready for occupation. She went and fetched the blue wrap, then

154

took Karen's soiled things through into the kitchen.

'It's time you went home, Patrick,' she said firmly. 'If you'll just refill the tank again after Miss Phillips has finished, I'll see to the coffee and food myself.'

Both the visitors were back in the living room when she eventually went through with the tray. Austin had on a pair of Dave's slacks, which didn't look too bad as he was quite tall himself, but the accompanying shirt swamped his narrower frame. His features were fine and regular, his hair over-long but bleached a pleasant blond by the sun. Kim judged him to be about twenty-seven and rather a different type from the men one usually met with in this country. At the moment he was looking distinctly uncomfortable.

'That's settled, then,' Dave was saying on a note of finality. 'Austin and myself will sleep up at the clubhouse, and you two girls can share this place. It might take a couple of days to get the road through again, so you'd better reconcile yourselves to roughing it while you wait.'

'Oh, it isn't *that* bad,' returned Karen equably. 'Should be quite an experience, in fact. Something to talk about when we get back. Did any of the others ever visit you on the mine, Dave?'

'Nobody else would be insane enough to think about it.' He was smiling back, voice taunting. 'Particularly for an afternoon.'

'We didn't intend to stay.'

'Obviously, or you'd have brought something with you. Still, now that you are here for a while we'll make the most of it.' His glance at Kim was

155

sardonic. 'I'm sure your company will be appreciated.'

'Is there any way of getting word through about what's happened?' asked Austin worriedly. 'We don't want search parties turning out to look for us.'

'It's been attended to.' Dave's tone was short. 'Have some coffee and stop thinking up non-existent problems.'

Austin flushed. 'Sorry. It only just occurred to me.' He sat down at Kim's side on the lounger, gave her a tentative smile. 'We must be making a lot of extra work for you.'

'If you are it's welcome,' she returned promptly. 'Visitors of any kind are so rare up here. Do you work with Ralph Tait?'

'I'm Bea's nephew—her brother's son. I only arrived a week ago for a month's vacation. She's been suggesting it for ages, but the opportunity never seemed to arise before this.' He added frankly, 'I've not done a lot of travelling outside of Britain and France, although I always promised myself I'd get further afield one day.'

'You seem to be keeping your promise. What are your impressions of Africa up to now?'

'Well, I wouldn't fancy living here permanently, but I wouldn't have missed coming. It's a fascinating continent. So many different cultures. I don't mind admitting that it isn't quite what I expected, though.' His quick grin was engaging. 'I suppose, deep down, I still saw it as wild, untrodden jungle peopled by savage hordes.'

'Austin is a born romantic,' drawled Karen without particular malice. 'I think he was quite disap-

156

pointed that we weren't making the trip up here on foot with native bearers, guns at the ready. I keep telling him that blowpipes went out with painted faces.'

Dave said dryly, 'You should try convincing some of the interior tribes about that.' He heaved himself to his feet. 'Time we were on our way. You girls can sort yourselves out all right, can't you?'

It was Kim who answered. 'Of course. We'll be fine.' She wished she could feel as sure as she sounded.

'Then we'll say goodnight. Bar the door as soon as we've gone.'

The sound of the engine had dwindled over the hill before either girl spoke. Karen was the first to break the silence.

'I suppose I should feel guilty about turfing Dave out of his own bed.'

'There's absolutely no need. The beds up at the club are perfectly comfortable.' Kim came back to the lounger and bent to the tray. 'More coffee?'

'I haven't finished this one, thanks.' Karen was sitting back in her chair, a cigarette between her fingers. 'You know, you're living in a fool's paradise,' she said conversationally. 'Dave might have given in to the necessity of a licence where you're concerned, but don't run away with the idea that a bit of paper is going to tie the two of you together for life. I've known him for two years. Long enough to realise that no one woman is ever going to own him.'

'Including yourself?' asked Kim softly.

The other shrugged. 'I wouldn't want to own any man. That's what gives me an edge over people like you. I'm of independent means, as they say, and not interested in settling down to the domestic life, so you can forget any ideas you might have about this being sour grapes on my part. I'm just warning you, that's all. With Dave nothing lasts. It's the way he is.'

'You came all this way just to tell me that?'

'No.' For a moment a smile touched her lips. 'I was curious about the set-up out here. Thought I'd kill two birds with one stone and give Austin a taste of adventure he's looking for so earnestly too. He's lived rather a restricted life, you know.'

Kim said quickly, 'I thought he seemed rather a nice person.'

'Oh, he is. Compared with that husband of yours he's a regular angel. That's what's so odd about women, though, isn't it? We don't go half as much for Austin's type, deserving though they are. I suppose it's something to do with the challenge. After all, anyone could handle Austin, but to bring a man like Dave Nelson to his knees ...' She laughed. 'Quite a thought, isn't it? I have to admit that I had a bit of a go myself at one point.'

'But now you're not interested?'

'I didn't say that. Dave may be a louse in some ways, but he's still the most exciting man I've met. I'd be a liar if I tried to make out that there was no attraction left between us, or that with you out of the way it mightn't flare up again for a while. You see, your husband and I have something unique in male–female relationships—understanding. No matter how long you manage to hang on to him you'll never be able to work out what makes him tick.'

There was too much truth in that statement for Kim to even attempt to deny it. All she wished was that people would stop pointing out to her what she already knew. She got abruptly to her feet and began to stack the tray. 'I'll go and make up your bed,' she said.

Austin arrived at the house at nine-thirty the following morning to find both girls up and dressed with breakfast an hour behind them. Dave had gone out to the scene of the landslide, he informed them. He had not said when he would be back.

'So how do we spend our day?' asked Karen. 'What do you normally do with your time, Kim, when the man of the house isn't here?'

Kim ignored the satire. 'I work,' she said equably. 'But not at the weekends. There's another car. I could take you round the site, if you like. Sunday is stand-down day.'

'Big deal. Still, I suppose anything is better than sitting around in this place. What's this club affair like, Austin?'

'All right.' He was hesitant to commit himself.

'It's only intended as somewhere for the men to get together during off-duty hours,' put in Kim defensively. 'They don't ask for a lot. We could have lunch there—providing you don't mind being stared at.'

'I never had any objections to being lusted after at a distance,' came the flippant reply. 'I hope you're a better driver than Austin, that's all. I don't fancy having to paddle again.'

The drive round the site could hardly be called a success. There was nothing very much of interest to the layman, and the mud made driving itself thoroughly hazardous. Kim's suggestion that they adjourn to the clubhouse for some refreshment met with the first show of enthusiasm of the morning from Karen, although Austin swore that he for one had enjoyed the tour.

Usually on a Sunday morning the club was fairly well patronised by those of the mine staff who had decided not to spend the weekend down in the town. Today, however, it appeared deserted. Kim left the other two sitting in the bar and went to find out where everyone was, finally running one of the club staff to earth in the dining room.

'All go out to roadway,' he informed her. 'More rock fall down.'

'So it's all hands to clearing the way back to civilisation,' commented Karen when Kim returned to her companions with the news. 'What say we run over and take a look for ourselves? I feel I have a bit of a personal stake on progress, after all.'

Kim hesitated, knowing full well that Dave would not like the idea of having mere idle sightseers around, yet aware of a growing urge to get out there herself. Something was wrong; she could feel it in her bones. A premonition of disaster of some kind.

'Afraid of what that husband of yours might say?' mocked Karen lightly. 'Don't worry, I'll take full responsibility. He knows what I'm like once I get my mind set on doing something. I'll even drive us up there, if you like.'

Kim made up her mind. 'Thanks,' she said shortly. 'but I'll do the driving myself.'

The main gates were flung open when they reached them, although the customary guard was on duty in the gatehouse. Kim drove straight through without waiting to get clearance and headed down the road towards the ravine with the sense of disaster growing stronger by the minute inside her. Round the bend lay a scene of utter disorder and confusion. The whole upper side of the mountain had given way over some seventy or eighty feet and spilled across the road, completely blocking it to traffic of any kind. Closer to where Kim stopped the car, a fresh fall had swept one of the huge electronic bulldozers to the edge of the ravine itself, turning it almost completely over so that it teetered within inches of crashing down the steep slope to the wooded floor a hundred feet below. There was more earth-moving equipment beyond, but no one manning it. Every man present seemed more concerned with saving the machine threatening to complete its roll and go over the edge, several of the men being engaged in rigging up some lifting gear while the others stood about in groups watching silently. Try as she might Kim failed to spot Dave among them, although she could see Luke directing operations on the rigging.

Her companions forgotten, she got out of the car and ran across to the burly engineer, pulling at his arm. 'Where is Dave?' she asked urgently, and knew the answer even as he turned to look at her with drawn face.

'He's under there,' he said, nodding towards the stricken dozer. 'He was driving it when the other lot came down right on top of him.'

Kim's breath caught in her throat. 'Is he dead?'

'No, but he's trapped.' He paused, then apparently decided to give it to her straight. 'If that machine moves another couple of inches it's going to crush him, and the way it's balanced it could go any minute.'

She looked from him to the bulldozer, to the half erected lifting gear and then back again to Luke. 'You have plenty of men here,' she said wildly. 'Can't they pull the machine off him without waiting for this?'

'Wouldn't work. It's got to be lifted from above. Got to be a straight lift too, which means we're going to have to get a chain right under. Can't take a chance of a hook slipping.' This time the pause held deliberation. 'Problem is how. What it really needs is for somebody to take the chain under and make sure it's fixed in exactly the right spot, only we don't have a man small enough to wriggle in without bringing the whole thing down on 'em both.'

'Dave got under all right that time when those other men were trapped,' she pointed out swiftly, and saw a faint, mirthless smile cross his features.

'Bit of a different proposition, this. The only reason Dave is still alive under there is because most of the weight is being taken by the cab frame —for the moment. If that goes, the whole lot goes, but right now it's creating enough of a space for a small wiry man to crawl through, if he's careful— only like I said, we don't have one that's small or wiry enough. Looks like we'll have to hook that chain through instead.'

And take the risk of destroying the precarious balance. He didn't have to say it; the knowledge hung between them in the sultry air. Kim said steadily, 'I'm small enough, Luke. I could take it through.'

'You?' He eyed her in sudden hopeful assessment, then slowly shook his head. 'Dave wouldn't have it. Too dangerous.'

'Dave is in no position to say *what* he will or won't have,' she returned, her resolve hardening. 'And unless someone does something quick he might not be in a position to say anything at all. You're in charge now, Luke. It's up to you to consider what's best.'

His regard was a study in indecision. 'You realise just how that thing is balanced? One wrong move, just one, and you'd have it down on top of the two of you.'

'I'll be careful. Just tell me what to do.'

Luke gave a couple of crisp orders to the men he was working with, then stepped nearer to the front of the machine, bending close to the ground to bring his face in line with the gap through which Kim would have to crawl. 'Dave, we're sending ... somebody through to get a chain round the middle,' he said in low but clear tones. 'Have you out of there in no time at all.'

Kim couldn't hear Dave's voice in reply, but Luke looked up at her and nodded. 'When you go in with the rope you'll have to make sure that the chain will have a free passage when we drag it through,' he said. 'The way Dave's lying it will have to go over his back as far as you can push it from this side, then you'll have to go in again from the other side and pull it across him. Still think you can make it?'

'I can try.' She was pale but determined. She

knelt on the earth at his side, thankful for the slacks which would make wriggling on her stomach over the rough ground at least a little easier than if she had been wearing a dress. The end of the rope —knotted so that she could hold it more securely— was in her hand. 'If I get stuck,' she added with an attempt at lightness, 'just grab a hold of my feet and yank me out!'

'Kim?' Dave's voice came with sudden surprising strength from below the machine. 'You keep out of here, do you hear me! Luke, get her away!'

Kim pulled a wry face at the other man before dropping flat on to her stomach in order to insert her head and shoulders slowly and carefully into the narrow space between metal and ground. She could make out the outline of the cab framework through which she was going to have to pass the rope, and Dave's body lying partly within it. He was on his side, with his left arm trapped by the upper part of the framework just below the elbow. His face was drawn into unfamiliar lines of strain, and his breathing sounded laboured. It was several seconds before she realised that the steady dripping sound came from the blood soaking through his shirt sleeve to fall in frighteningly large drops on to the metal below.

There was very little room to manoeuvre, and none at all to turn in. Kim dare not use the metal-work itself to pull herself along by, but could manage to move a few inches at a time by pushing with her elbows against the ground. The rope lay beneath her, running back between her knees to where Luke was paying it carefully out as she moved. It took her five endless minutes to reach a

164

position from where she could ease the rope from under her body and reach out with it across Dave's waist.

'Can you possibly get your other hand down to stop it from pulling back when I go out again?' she asked softly. She wiped the perspiration from her face with the collar of her shirt, keeping her limbs rigid in the confined space, hearing the groaning complaint of the slowly buckling metal with thudding heart and a prayer silently on her lips. Just let it hold out a little longer!

Dave slid his arm down his side and grasped the rope end firmly, his fingers cold against hers. His face was grey, his jaw set rigid against the pain. 'You shouldn't be here,' he gritted. 'I told you to stay out of it.'

'I know.' Kim's hand lingered for a brief moment over his, feeling the clenching of his knuckles. 'You can read the riot act later. I'll see you in a few minutes from the other side.'

Backing out was even more difficult than getting in. By the time she had wriggled her way to freedom she was wet through, and exhausted with the sheer effort of moving in such a fashion in that heat, but there was still the rest of the job to accomplish.

'Have a rest,' advised Luke, looking concerned at her appearance. 'Give it a minute or two before you go in again.'

'There's no time.' She stood up unsteadily. 'That cab isn't going to hold up much longer, and the way the framework is resting on Dave's arm ...' She left the rest unsaid, reluctant to put into words the full horror of what would inevitably happen should the full weight of the bulldozer descend on the trapped man. 'There's another thing, too, Luke. Do you think I might be able to pull the chain through myself when I go in the other side? It could easily become caught up in the framework if someone isn't there to guide it.'

'It's heavy,' he said doubtfully. 'And you'll be pulling flat on your stomach.'

'All right then, so I'll fetch the rope through first, then go back in to see to the chain while you do the pulling from out here. Once we've got it round the frame it should be safe.'

The minutes all seemed to run into one another after that. Thinking about it afterwards, Kim could never recall the exact details of her last journey into the foot-high passage to lift the chain as it was pulled through by Luke and his helpers and guide it safely into position for the lift, nor of her subsequent return to the open air. The only thing she did remember with any clarity was the trembling weakness of her limbs as Luke helped her to her feet, and the reassuring sight of the heavy chain being hoisted up to the waiting hook. Then there was the tension of watching the lifting gear take the strain, the groaning of metal as the front of the dozer rose slowly inch by inch into the air until there was clearance enough for a couple of men to rush in and lift Dave out from under the bar which had held him so securely. Seconds later came an earth-jarring crash as the hastily rigged mounting gave up the unequal battle with gravitational pull and collapsed on top of the machine, to slide with it into the ravine.

Dave was still conscious when they laid him on

the waiting stretcher. The mine's doctor gave him an injection of morphine before ripping back the blood-soaked sleeve to above the elbow. Kim saw the slight compression of his jaw as he viewed the damage, and bit down hard on the question which sprang involuntarily to her lips. Luke caught her eyes, his expression revealing his own assessment. He had seen injuries like that before.

The morphine had taken effect by the time they were ready to load the stretcher into the back of one of the cars. There was a glazed look in the grey eyes when Kim climbed in and sat beside him, a vulnerability about his mouth which made her want to put her own to it, not in passion but in comfort. Dave was no fool. He knew the implications in Doctor Selby's evasive comment, and no amount of morphine was going to dull that kind of fear. His good hand lay on the stretcher bare inches from her own as she sat on the narrow seat, but she made no attempt to touch it. Something within her sensed that at this moment he would not want to be touched—not by her, not by anyone. His kind had to fight fear alone. She just sat there in silence with her eyes on the dirt-streaked face of the man she had married for the duration of the journey up to the mine's hospital.

She was still waiting for news when Luke came to join her in the little ante-room some time later. She accepted his offer of a cigarette gratefully, resting her head against the wall at her back as she smoked it, her eyes closed wearily. Dave was going to come through this all right. He had to come through it. His work was his life—the only kind of life he knew or wanted. Deprived of it he would only be half a man.

'You love him, don't you?' Luke's voice was gruff. 'I thought you only married him for a meal ticket.'

Her eyes had come open, but she didn't look at him. 'I'm not sure that love is the right word,' she said. 'Not as I've always understood it. How can you love someone you don't even know, Luke?'

'Never thought about it,' he admitted. 'I'm just a man. It's only you women who get all tied up about things like that. I never did understand your sex, if it comes to that. You can't have a simple relationship; there always has to be complications.'

She was looking at him now, studying the rugged features as though she had never really seen them before. 'You think that's what I'm doing—complicating matters?'

'Yes,' he stated bluntly. 'You just risked your life for that man in there. If that isn't love I don't know what is. If I'd ever found a woman willing to do that for me I'd have been sure enough of her feelings.'

She said softly, 'Do you think Dave will be sure of mine for him?'

He hesitated. 'Not necessarily. There's one or two things you should know about him, maybe, before you go any further. Things I've only learned about him myself by reading between the lines. He never had a home or family of his own, you see. His parents were killed in an accident when he was a couple of years old and he spent his life in a succession of foster-homes till he was old enough to fend for himself. I remember him saying once when he was off guard that after the first two he daren't let himself get too fond of the people he lived with because of the fear of being taken away again. Growing up with that kind of restriction is bound to have some effect on a man.'

'You mean Dave isn't as hard as he makes out.'

'Something like that. I'd say he'd have to be more than sure of a woman's feelings for him before he'd start to give an inch in her direction. Even more so now this has happened.'

Kim's mouth was dry. 'You're so sure he's going to lose his arm?'

'Let's say I'm not counting on anything better. And if he does lose it my bet is that the first thing he's going to do when he wakes up is give you your marching orders. Only you can decide whether you feel enough for him to stick by him anyway, but believe me he needs you, Kim. He's been a different man this last few weeks. For once in his life he's had a home of his own to come back to after a day's work, a woman to share it with. That's meant something to him no matter how much he's tried to hide it.' He paused, his eyes on her face. 'Think you could face the kind of hell he's liable to put you through before you break him down?'

'I'm not sure,' she confessed unhappily. 'Luke. I'm just not sure.'

'Then you'd better make up your mind. And fast. Only don't make any mistake about it. One thing he isn't going to need is pity.'

She knew he was right. This was something she had to work out for herself. Did she love Dave enough to face up to the inevitable battle with his pride and independence if the worst came to the worst, or would it be better, and fairer on them both if she took the easy way out and accepted the alternative Luke was so certain would be offered her? Was what she felt for Dave anything to do with love at all, if it came to that?

The answer took no searching for. All she had to do was recall the moment when Luke had told her that Dave was trapped under the bulldozer, the emotions which had swept blindingly through her in that second or two before she had known he was still alive. There had been no doubt or hesitation in her mind then. All she had known was the need to get to him, to have him safe.

But there was more to this than just her own emotions, she thought. No matter what Luke believed about Dave's feelings for her it didn't have to follow that he was right. And if Dave did tell her to go would she have the courage to refuse with that doubt inside her?

CHAPTER EIGHT

HOURS seemed to pass before Doctor Selby finally
came out to where they waited. He looked tired
and strained, and there was an odd air of reticence
about him as he looked at Kim.

'He's going to be all right,' he said into the waiting silence. 'The arm's broken and cut about, but
it wasn't as bad as I first feared. He's awake, and
asking to see you.'

Dave was lying propped up slightly on a couple
of pillows when Kim went through to the narrow
ward containing half a dozen beds. His face was
pale beneath the tan, but the grey eyes were as
aware as ever. The injured left arm was in a cast
from below the elbow and supported in a canvas
sling held by a frame over the bed.

'Glad to hear the good news,' she said. 'Doctor
Selby said you wanted to see me.'

'Yes.' His voice was low but steady. 'I didn't
thank you for saving my life earlier on.'

'They'd have got you out one way or another,'
she returned diffidently. 'How do you feel?'

'I'll live.' He studied her hardily. 'I don't have to
tell you that this changes plans, of course. I'll be
staying on here till my contract runs out, but
there's no reason for you to wait around any
longer. There's a flight out tomorrow afternoon.
Luke will get a 'copter out and see you on to the

plane, and I'll arrange a draft to your bank till we get things sorted out. Don't worry about anything. You'll be taken care of.'

'Paying me off?' Kim was amazed at her own control.

'If you want to see it that way.'

She swallowed dryly. 'Supposing I don't want to go?'

His eyes narrowed. 'What are you after—more money?'

'As I don't know how much you were thinking of offering me I could scarcely be asking for more,' she rejoined. 'You ... promised me a trip south before we went back to England.'

Lips twisting, he indicated the injured arm. 'With this?'

'I can drive.'

The harsh intake of his breath was clearly audible in the quietness of the room. 'If you think I need a woman to look after me you've got another think coming. So far as I'm concerned it's all over between us, green eyes, so the sooner you're out of here the better. It was going to finish anyway in a week or two.'

'It still could—if you wanted it to.' She forced herself to make a final effort. 'I—I don't want to go, Dave. Not like this. Can't we stick to the original plan and at least travel back home together?'

There was no hint of softening in the grey eyes. 'No,' he stated flatly, 'we can't. I just got through telling you that you're not wanted around any more.'

'Just because you've broken an arm? That hardly seems ...'

172

'The arm is only a part of it.' His jaw was taut, his mouth a hard line. 'Can't you get it through your head that I've had enough of the whole affair? Sure I said we'd take a trip south. That was before...' He paused, went on again with deliberation, 'Before I met up with Karen again. As soon as this cast is off any plans I make will be including her. Does that make it clear enough for you?'

Kim's chin lifted, her own pride fighting to conceal the pain inside her. 'It couldn't be clearer. Don't worry, Dave, I won't cause you any trouble. You don't even need to see me again. I hope you both find what you're looking for.'

She turned away with as much dignity as she could muster and walked out of the ward. It was over. Dave didn't want her. Luke had been wrong.

'Kim?' Luke came towards her as she stumbled over the single step leading down into the room where she had left him waiting. 'What is it? What happened?'

'Where is Karen?' she asked unsteadily.

'I suggested the pair of them should go back to the house,' he said, and there was a sudden leap of understanding in his eyes. 'Is that what he's doing —using her as an excuse to get you to leave?'

'Not an excuse. A reason. It's Karen he wants, not me.' Kim gave him a stiff-lipped smile. 'You were wrong, Luke. Dave doesn't *need* anybody. He never will. He's just made that only too plain.'

Luke was silent for a long moment, a variety of expressions chasing across his face. His shrug held defeat. 'Sorry,' he said. 'I could have sworn I knew him better than that. Come on, I'll take you back to the house.'

Karen came to the door at the sound of the car, Austin behind her.

'Well?' she demanded as Kim came up the steps with Luke at her side. 'What's the verdict?'

'He's going to be all right. His arm is broken, but that's all.' Kim walked past the two of them, aware of the speculation in the other girl's eyes as she followed. 'There's no reason why you shouldn't go up to see him, if you want to. He's quite himself again.'

'He is?' Karen was still not quite certain of the message her senses were registering. 'Did he say he wanted to see me?'

'Yes.' Kim's voice was quietly controlled as she added, 'I shall be leaving in the morning. I'm going home to England. I'll see about some food. We never did get that lunch.'

Luke followed her through into the kitchen, leaning a hand against the door-jamb in a way which made her heart turn over painfully. 'You're going to go?' he said. 'Just like that.'

'What else am I supposed to do?' She looked back at him numbly. 'He hasn't left me any choice. He wants me out of here as soon as possible. Incidentally, you're supposed to be seeing me on to the plane tomorrow, via helicopter from here.'

'Well, I can scotch that for a start.'

'It won't do any good. If you refuse to take me in he'll simply get one of the other men to do it for him. I'd rather be with you.'

He regarded her helplessly. 'I just don't get it. If there'd been anything seriously wrong with that arm I'd have expected this, but not as it is.'

'It's quite simple,' she said. 'Dave is tired of me

and wants out. The accident just brought things to a head rather sooner, that's all. I knew from the start that it wasn't a permanent arrangement. Dave isn't springing any surprises. It's only me who changed.'

'What will you do when you get back?'

'I'm not sure. Accept his offer of money till I find myself a job, I suppose. I don't really have any other choice. But I'll pay him back every penny,' she added fiercely.

Luke made a small exasperated movement of his head. 'You know, you're as proud as he is—and as stubborn! I'll bet you never even tried to tell him how you feel about him.'

'Tried?' Kim whipped round to face him, green eyes over-bright. 'Luke, he doesn't want to know! There's only one thing he's interested in, and that's getting rid of me as soon as possible. He hates the thought of me having been the one to go under that darned machine with the chain, for one thing. I think he would almost preferred to go with it rather than owe anything to a woman.'

'Then it's time he had his ideas straightened out,' was the tight-lipped reply, and Luke straightened away from the door-jamb. 'Broken arm or not, he's going to get a few home truths rammed down his throat!'

'No, please.' She put a staying hand on his arm. 'Just leave it, will you? For my sake.'

There was a pause, then he wryly shook his head. 'All right, if it means that much to you. I'd better go and make arrangements to get a 'copter out here in the morning. What about the other two? Think they'll be wanting a lift down at the same time? It could be another couple of days before the road's useable again.'

'I'm not sure. You'd better ask them.' She turned away again, reaching for a tray. 'Stay and have some coffee with us first.'

Austin jumped at the chance to get back to the coast, obviously having had quite enough of roughing it for the present. Karen also acknowledged a desire for the refinements of the Tait household. She didn't find it necessary to add that she could always come back. The complacency in her smile was enough to make that particular point. She got up when Luke rose to leave after they had finished eating, and asked Kim for the loan of the car to go across to the hospital.

'I suppose I should look in on our invalid before we leave,' she said lightly. 'And there may not be time in the morning. Perhaps you wouldn't mind pointing me in the right direction, Luke?'

'Sure,' acknowledged the latter briefly as Kim handed over the keys. 'Come on.'

Austin kept his eyes on his plate for several moments after the other two had departed, his face a little flushed. Kim felt sorry for him. He had been landed right in the middle of a situation he couldn't even begin to understand, and through no fault of his own. She could quite appreciate his discomfiture and uncertainty as to how to act. The only way to ease the atmosphere was to bring the whole thing out into the open, she decided.

'I'm sorry you had to be involved in all this, Austin,' she said quietly. 'But as you are it might be better to get the story into its proper perspective. Dave and I were breaking up anyway very shortly.

Under the circumstances it simply seemed more sensible to make the break now.'

'You don't have to explain anything,' he said, finally looking at her. 'I know I'm not a very worldly person, and I'm not going to pretend that I understand what's happened between you and Dave, but one thing I do know is that you're letting Karen walk all over you. She told me on the way up here that she intended to get Dave back, even if it was only for the pleasure of taking him off you. She doesn't really want him herself. Quite honestly, I don't think she's capable of wanting anything or anyone for longer than it takes her to get them. She's a very ... selfish person.'

Kim smiled at him faintly. 'And you're a very nice one, Austin. You may even be right about Karen, only she wasn't the real cause of the trouble. The simple truth is that Dave and I just aren't suited. We'll both of us be far happier apart.' Her voice lightened deliberately. 'So having got that out of the way, let's forget it and have some more coffee.'

They were talking about Austin's home life when Karen returned some time later. She seemed different somehow, Kim thought, though it wasn't a change she could put a finger on. Yes, Dave was in good spirits, the other girl informed her. She said it in a detached sort of way, as if her thoughts were elsewhere. Austin had probably hit the nail right on the head when he had delineated Karen's character, she reflected. Now that she had won Karen was losing interest in the chase. She supposed she should feel glad that Dave was probably going to get a taste of his own medicine, but she couldn't. Her only comfort lay in the knowledge that when it came to depth of emotion Karen and he made a good pair. Neither of them could be badly hurt. At this moment it seemed a trait to envy.

It rained throughout the night, only letting up at dawn. The skies remained overcast for an hour or so with thunder grumbling distantly, then miraculously cleared. By the time Luke came to collect them the red mud of the clearing was already hardening again beneath the fierce heat of the sun. Kim didn't look back as the car headed up the slope away from the house she had lived in for the past month. It belonged now to a part of her life she was going to shut out of her mind for always—if she could. She was going home.

The helicopter was already waiting for them on the landing strip beside the main gates. Kim's heart gave a sudden lurch as she recognised the pilot, and it was with some difficulty that she kept the smile on her face as they came up to the machine. He gave her a curious look when he helped her up to take a seat at his side, but to her relief made no comment about their previous meeting. Luke climbed in behind her and slid along the door, settling himself on the bench seat as the motor sprang to life. Then they were rising into the air, sliding upwards and sideways towards the ridge, the sprawl of buildings and great tracts of excavated earth passing rapidly from sight until there was only forest below.

They had been flying for some minutes before Jerry Brice finally spoke.

'I didn't expect to have you as a passenger today,'

he said in low tones to Kim. 'Coming back, are you?'

'No,' she said, aware that Karen was listening in from her seat behind them. 'No, I'm not coming back.'

He glanced round at her, noting the smudges under her eyes, the strain around her mouth. 'You don't strike me as the type to run out on a man who's down,' he said unexpectedly. 'After what's happened to Dave I'd have thought you'd want to stick around.'

'He only has a broken arm,' she returned defensively.

'Oh?' He sounded surprised. 'That's not how I heard it. One of the guys I was talking to a bit back seemed to think he was in pretty bad shape. Said the doc's boy had told him it might still have to come off.'

Kim sat very still, her heart thudding against her rib cage. 'He must have got it wrong.'

'Maybe. Seemed sure enough about it, though.'

Some instinct turned Kim's head round until her eyes met Karen's. The other girl looked straight back at her without flinching, but she couldn't quite conceal the expression which flitted briefly across her face.

'You knew, didn't you?' Kim said softly. 'That's why you were so offhand when you came back last night. He told you the truth.'

'He didn't; Doctor Selby did.' Karen's voice was careless. 'If you want the truth, I never actually saw Dave at all. There didn't seem much point. I've no intention of getting myself tied up with a cripple.'

The cruelty of her words barely registered; it

was the meaning behind them which took Kim by the throat. 'Dave would never be a cripple,' she shot out. 'No matter what happens he'll never be that!' She transferred her attention forward again, refusing to stop and consider what she was about to do, knowing only that she had to do it. 'Jerry, will you take me back? Please. It's important.'

He was turning the machine even as she spoke, coming round in a wide sweep which would bring them back on course for the mine again. 'This is going to mess up my next job,' he said, smiling, 'but what the hell! I'll book it as running repairs.'

They were back at the site within minutes, although to Kim the return journey seemed to take an age. It still wasn't wholly certain that Dave wanted her, but the very fact that he had obviously told Doctor Selby to pass on false information about the state of his injury required explanation. That pride of his would have been all the reason he needed for sending her away. Dave would not have been able to face the possibility of having her stay with him out of pity alone. And it was going to be no less difficult convincing him that pity had played no part in her return, she realised. His barriers had been up too long to be broken down easily.

Luke got out of the cabin with her when they landed, hoisting out her suitcase. Kim said a brief farewell to the two passengers in the back, and received a shrug of the shoulders from Karen by way of reply.

'Good luck,' said Austin with sincerity. 'I hope everything turns out all right.'

Kim touched his hand, then smiled at the pilot.

'Thanks, Jerry.'

'My pleasure,' he said.

The helicopter was already airborne by the time the two of them reached the car. Kim waved a hand, and saw Austin wave back. Then they were gone, and Luke was starting the engine, heading for the road up to the hospital.

'It isn't going to be easy,' he said, voicing her own thoughts. 'He'll be glad to see you back, but he'll not admit it.'

'I'll cope,' she said. 'He can say what he likes. I'm staying this time.'

Luke smiled, 'Good lass!'

Doctor Selby was in the treatment room sorting out the contents of his bag. He looked at Kim in some surprise when she appeared in the doorway, glancing at his watch.

'I thought you'd left,' he said. 'Didn't your transport turn up?'

'Yes.' There was time for explanations later, Kim decided. At the moment she wanted only to get the situation clear. 'Is it true that Dave is in danger of losing that arm?'

The doctor's expression underwent a change. 'Who told you that?' he demanded.

'It doesn't matter who told me. I just want to know if it's true.'

There was a brief pause, then he sighed suddenly and nodded. 'Yes, it's true—or at least the possibility is there. Even at the best it's doubtful that he'll ever use it properly again. The nerves were severed. I did the best I could, but...' He left the rest in the air. 'I didn't like doing what I did, only he wouldn't have you know the truth. Personally, I thought he was wrong to keep it from you.'

'You told Karen—the young woman you saw last night.'

'Also at Dave's instigation. He asked me to collar her before she could get through to the ward and make sure that she knew exactly what the position was. Said it was the surest way he knew of getting rid of her.'

'I see.' Kim tried to steady her nerves. It wasn't over yet. Not by a long chalk. 'Is it all right if I go through and see him?'

'By all means.' The doctor shook his head wryly. 'Although I wouldn't like to hazard a guess as to how he'll react when he sees you. I doubt that there's anybody knows the way Dave Nelson's mind works!'

Kim hoped there was one person. Luke's judgement was all she could put her faith in now.

One of the Africans was about to enter the ward with a mug of coffee. Kim took it from him, motioning him to silence as she pushed open the door. Dave was standing at the window with his back to the room. He was fully dressed and wore his left arm in a sling. He didn't turn at her entry, simply inclined his head towards the bedside locker. 'Put it down there, will you?'

Heart beating fast, Kim walked over and slid the mug down on to the locker top, her hand and arm coming into his line of vision as she did so. His head came round abruptly, and for a long, quivering moment there was a complete silence in the room as he stared at her. The flash of expression in the grey eyes was so brief that Kim could not be sure she had seen them change at all, then the barriers were up once more, his thoughts impossible to read.

'The helicopter left twenty minutes ago,' he said harshly. 'Why aren't you on it?'

'I was.' Kim was hard put not to show any betraying quiver. 'I asked Jerry to bring me back.'

'Why?' The word was shot at her.

'Because of something I found out. Something Karen confirmed for me.' She paused. 'Dave, I have a right to know the truth too. What you made Doctor Selby do was unfair, both to him and to me.'

A muscle jerked suddenly in his jawline. 'It's a matter of opinion. Anyway, it makes no difference except that you've created more problems by coming back like this. Now we're going to have to fetch Jerry Brice out here again.'

'Not today you're not. He's got a full schedule.'

'So? His firm has other machines.' He moved jerkily to lean his weight against the windowsill. 'One thing is certain, you're not staying here. I told you once to get out.'

'Scared you can't handle me with only one arm?' she asked with deliberation, and saw his mouth compress.

'Sure,' he said, 'that's it. I can feel sorry enough for myself without *your* contribution.'

She smiled a little. 'Oh, don't worry, I've no intention of feeling sorry for you. Why should I? Doctor Selby says it isn't one hundred per cent certain that you're going to suffer any lasting effects from that arm, and even if the worst did come to the worst you'd teach yourself to do as much with one good arm as most men could do with three! The trouble with you, Dave Nelson, is that you suspect everybody's motives. Did it ever occur to you that I might want to stay with you for quite another reason?'

His lips twisted. 'Such as?'

'Such as the fact that I might be in love with you,' she said huskily. 'And don't look like that. It happens to be true. I didn't want to love you. It just ... happened that way.'

'You couldn't help yourself?' There was mockery in his voice, in the hard smile curving his lips. 'Good try, green eyes, but I'm not that much of a fool. Attracted you might be, despite yourself, but don't confuse *that* kind of feeling with love. All I am is the man who happened to be the first one to make you realise you were a woman.'

'You made me realise a whole lot of things,' she came back swiftly. 'I kept telling myself that I hated you, but it was only because I was ashamed to admit that I wanted you as much as you kept telling me I did. Wanting is a part of loving, Dave. At least it is for a woman—*my* kind of woman.'

There was no softness in the grey eyes studying her. 'Why wait till now to tell me all this? Why not yesterday, or the day before?'

The next took a lot of saying, but she did it with scarcely a pause. 'Because I wasn't sure of your feelings for me then.'

'And you are now?'

'I ... think so.' She made a small gesture of appeal with one hand going out towards him. 'Dave, I've been honest with you at the cost of my own pride. Can't you come at least halfway to meet me?'

His shrug was coolly deliberate. 'Sorry. I'm not

in the market for happy endings.'

Kim looked into the stony, unrelenting features and knew a sudden flare of pure white-hot anger which brought the words tumbling from her lips without consideration. 'Then you're a fool!' she flung at him. 'And so am I for even hoping that I might be able to get through that thick hide of yours! You know what else you are, Dave? You're a coward! You're so darned terrified of giving anyone even the slightest bit of an edge on you that you'd die rather than act like a human being for once! Well, I'm not sure that I want a coward for a husband. I might have thought you all sorts of a swine when we first met, but it never occurred to me that you lacked courage. You spend the rest of your life being afraid of getting hurt, if you like. I'm going to find myself a man with enough guts to take a few risks!'

Half blinded by tears, she stumbled across the room to the door, putting out a hand gropingly to find the handle. She hadn't heard him move after her, but suddenly his hand was on her shoulder, spinning her about and pinning her against the door-jamb. His face was white, his eyes blazing.

'I'll kill you for that,' he gritted. 'You damned little...' His hand moved savagely from her shoulder to her throat, bruising the flesh as he jerked up her head. Then his mouth was on hers in brutal demand, brooking no resistance, claiming possession. Kim made no attempt to fight him. Instead she responded, giving back measure for measure as far as she was capable until at last the hardness of his lips began to relax and move with softer passion against hers, his hand releasing its grasp on her throat to slide around her and pull her to him. She clung to him desperately, the tears still wet on her cheeks, not thinking of anything but the moment. When he finally lifted his head she laid her cheek against his chest, feeling the strong beat of his heart, the warmth of his breath in her hair.

'I love you,' she said. 'You've got to believe it, Dave. I love you!'

'I want to believe it.' For the first time since she had known him there was uncertainty in his voice. 'I can't tell you how much I want to. This last few weeks since you turned up I've felt ... like somebody with a new lease of life. I'm not going to pretend that I intended you nothing but good from the start. I wanted you, and I used every advantage I had to get you, but I never looked any further ahead than the time it was going to take to get you back to England.'

'You thought you'd have had enough of me by then?' she murmured.

'I suppose so, if I thought about it at all.' His hand in her hair was gentle yet still with a touch of restraint. 'You were different from any other woman I'd met. Your loyalty to Adams, for instance, even when you knew what had happened. And the way you took it when he showed you what he was really worth. Never a tear till you'd left the house, and then only because it suddenly came over you what a mess you were in. After that I didn't stop to consider anything but my own interests. I knew I wouldn't get you any other way, so I came up with the idea of offering you a temporary marriage— only I didn't make any allowances for that trusting nature of yours.' He paused, held her away from him, eyes searching her face. 'Did you really believe that any man could be *that* altruistic?'

'I don't know.' Her smile was faintly wavery. 'Perhaps I wanted to convince myself—an excuse, like you said.'

'I said a whole lot of things I'd rather forget.' His own smile was wry. 'God only knows how you can finish up feeling anything for me at all after the way I've handled you, but that iceberg act was like a red rag to a bull. That night you offered to give yourself to me in return for Adams's safety I could have killed you both!'

'But you knew what I really felt when you made love to me,' she pointed out. 'You told me yourself that I was only being stubborn.'

'Sure I did. It was one thing to feel that the barriers were there because of your determination to hold out against me, something else again to know that they'd been dropped in repayment of a debt. That was when I knew that I wasn't going to be able to just walk away when the time came. I suggested that trip south in the hope that somewhere along the line we could come to some kind of understanding and start over again.'

Kim glanced down at the stiffened left arm, said softly, 'Then this happened and you immediately saw yourself as a liability no woman could possibly want to take on. Oh, Dave, you must have been blind not to have realised what you were doing to me when you told me to go away.' She looked up into the grey eyes again. 'You do believe it now, don't you?'

'Yes,' he said. 'Yes, I believe it. Only you're going to have your work cut out keeping me this con-

187

vinced, I'm warning you. It's going to take a few thousand kisses like the one you just gave me to start with, and from there...' His own glance dropped to his arm and his smile went a little crooked ... 'from there we'll have to make it up as we go along. Three arms between two people sounds reasonable.'

'Four sounds even better,' she returned steadily. 'Doctor Selby's is only one opinion, and he'd be the first to admit that he's scarcely infallible. There are surgeons in England far better qualified to give the casting vote, and even then a lot will probably depend on your own will power—and heaven knows you have plenty of that!'

Dave was looking at her with an intent expression, as though trying to implant every line of her features on his memory. 'And if it does turn out for the worst?'

'Then you'll have to get a tin one,' she retorted promptly. 'And I'll just have to remember which one not to bite!'

His sudden laugh was pure enjoyment, hearty and masculine and without restriction. Arm about her waist, he swung her off her feet and level with his mouth, holding her there effortlessly. 'Remind me to tell you some time that I love you, green eyes,' he said. 'But for now just let's concentrate on this!'

Mills & Boon Classics

The very best of Mills & Boon
romances, brought back for those of you
who missed reading them when they
were first published.

There are three other Classics for you to collect this
December

THE BEADS OF NEMESIS
by Elizabeth Hunter

Pericles Holmes had married Morag Grant as a matter of
convenience, but she had lost no time in falling in love
with him. Whereupon her beautiful stepsister Delia, who
always got everything she wanted, announced that she
wanted Pericles!

HEART OF THE LION
by Roberta Leigh

When Philippa encouraged young Cathy Joyce to elope,
she didn't know the girl was the niece of her boss, the
formidable newspaper tycoon Marius Lyon — but that
didn't stop him promptly giving her the sack. But that
was by no means the last of Marius as far as Philippa
was concerned!

THE RAINBOW BIRD
by Margaret Way

Paige Norton was visiting the vast Benedict cattle empire
as the guest of Joel Benedict. She had looked forward
to it immensely, although she hadn't much liked the
sound of Joel's stepbrother Ty, the boss of the station.
And when she met Ty, she liked the reality even less . . .

If you have difficulty in obtaining any of these books through
your local paperback retailer, write to:

Mills & Boon Reader Service
P.O. Box 236, Thornton Road, Croydon, Surrey, CR9 3RU.

Mills & Boon Classics

The very best of Mills & Boon
romances, brought back for those of you
who missed reading them when they
were first published

In
January
we bring back the following four
great romantic titles.

FAMILIAR STRANGER
by Lilian Peake

Adrienne was determined to marry her fiancé, Clifford Denning
— but was 'determination' the right attitude to take to something
as important as marriage? Clifford's brother Murray kept warning
her that she was heading for disaster but why should she listen to
that overbearing Murray?

BRIDE'S DILEMMA
by Violet Winspear

Tina married John Trecarrel in haste — and had time to repent
when she found out that she had to compete with the memory
of his beautiful first wife and that he was attracted to Joanna's
equally beautiful cousin Paula.

THE YELLOW MOON
by Rebecca Stratton

It was going to break Catherine's heart to be forced to send her
two adored little half-brothers to live with their unknown Greek
uncle on his Greek island home. Then it appeared that this uncle
was planning to take over Catherine's life as well . . .

WITCHSTONE
by Anne Mather

When Ashley's father died she travelled northwards to live with
her uncle and aunt in their hotel. There she met Jake, to whom she
was attracted, but who had to be remote for many reasons . . .
most of all because of his forthcoming marriage to Barbara.

If you have difficulty in obtaining any of these books through
your local paperback retailer, write to:

Mills & Boon Reader Service
P.O. Box 236, Thornton Road, Croydon, Surrey, CR9 3RU.

Masquerade
Historical Romances

Intrigue excitement romance

A PERFECT MATCH
by Julia Murray

Louisa married Simon, Lord Winslow, very reluctantly indeed, and she knew that he had only offered for her to preserve the proprieties. So why should he interfere with her innocent attempts to help his unhappy brother-in-law, Henry Landry?

FRENCHMAN'S HARVEST
by Emma Gayle

Helen Caister agreed to visit her mother's old home — a château in the Médoc region of France — only because she had fallen in love with her cousin, Marc d'Auray, and could not refuse his invitation. But Marc cared only for his inheritance and his precious vines . . .

Look out for these titles in your local paperback shop from 12th December 1980